KU-662-218

CONTENTS

Introduction

The Smoking Debate is the thirty-eighth volume in the Issues series. The aim of this series is to offer up-to-date information about important issues in our world.

The Smoking Debate looks at children and smoking, smoking in the workplace and passive smoking. It also has a chapter on quitting smoking.

The information comes from a wide variety of sources and includes:
Government reports and statistics
Newspaper reports and features
Magazine articles and surveys
Literature from lobby groups
and charitable organisations.

It is hoped that, as you read about the many aspects of the issues explored in this book, you will critically evaluate the information presented. It is important that you decide whether you are being presented with facts or opinions. Does the writer give a biased or an unbiased report? If an opinion is being expressed, do you agree with the writer?

The Smoking Debate offers a useful starting-point for those who need convenient access to information about the many issues involved. However, it is only a starting-point. At the back of the book is a list of organisations which you may want to contact for further information.

*****

The Smoking Debate

ISSUES

Volume 38

Independence

Educational Publishers

Cambridge

First published by Independence
PO Box 295
Cambridge CB1 3XP
England

British Library Cataloguing in Publication Data
The Smoking Debate – (Issues Series)
I. Donnellan, Craig II. Series
362.2'96

ISBN 1 86168 193 3

Printed in Great Britain
The Burlington Press
Cambridge

Typeset by
Claire Boyd

Cover
The illustration on the front cover is by
Pumpkin House.

Smoking trends in the UK

Information from the Cancer Research Campaign

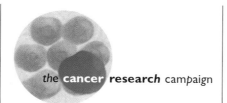

In the UK, the smoking epidemic among men reached a peak in the 1940s when two-thirds of all men smoked. This proportion remained high until the early 1970s. Since then, thanks to health education, it has fallen steadily and now only 26% of adult men smoke. Among women, smoking only became a common habit after the Second World War. From a peak of two-fifths (41%) throughout 1948 to 1980, the smoking rate has now dropped to 26%. Smoking is highest among those aged 16-24: 35% of women and 38% of men in this age-group smoke.

Lung cancer takes perhaps 20 years to develop and is usually fatal, so we are still seeing the effects of the UK smoking epidemic in the large number of lung cancer deaths. These are now falling in all age groups for men, reflecting the earlier trend for giving up smoking. But for older women, sadly, lung cancer deaths are still rising. In the UK lung cancer is still the biggest killer cancer.

Smoking trends among children and young people

According to the latest figures from the Office for National Statistics, 21% of 15-year-olds are regular smokers. Many of these teenage smokers are already addicted to nicotine, that is, they need to smoke their first cigarette for the day as soon as they get up. Smoking is particularly popular with teenage girls: 11% of teenage girls are regular smokers compared with 8% of boys.

Eight out of ten smokers start under the age of 20 and the majority wish they had never started. More than 7 out of 10 current smokers say they want to quit. Very worryingly, 30% of mothers-to-be risk their own health and that of their unborn child

through tobacco use. So education to prevent smoking needs to start before young people take up the habit and before they contemplate parenthood.

Socio-economic trends

More smokers from higher social classes quit the habit when smoking

Eight out of ten smokers begin under the age of 20 and the majority wish they had never started

declined from the 1970s on. This means that a disproportionate number of smokers are from lower socio-economic groups. The plight of low income smokers has been discussed in many reports: it is far more difficult to quit when faced with problems of poor housing, unemployment and poverty. There need to be targeted programmes to help low income smokers which take account of their special needs.

It is worrying that recent reports suggest an increase in smoking among young people from more affluent groups. Unless effective measures are taken, this could lead to a reversal in the earlier smoking decline with its consequent damaging effects to the health of the nation.

• The above information is an extract from the Cancer Research Campaign's web site which can be found at www.crc.org.uk Alternatively, see page 41 for their address details.

© The Cancer Research Campaign

Smoking: the facts

You may not be one of the ten million smokers in the UK but are you also at risk? *Asthma News* takes a hard look at the facts behind smoking.

The smoker

Ms Smith is 38 years of age. She smokes 20 cigarettes a day. She enjoys smoking because it makes her feel more relaxed and confident. Although she knows that smoking is bad for her, she would rather turn a blind eye to the following facts…

Toxic habit

- She is inhaling over 4,000 toxins, 43 of which are known to cause cancer.
- The nicotine in her cigarette increases her blood pressure, makes her heart beat faster and damages her circulatory system.
- The carbon monoxide in her cigarette replaces oxygen in her blood. This makes her blood stickier and puts a strain on her heart.
- Tar is sticking to her windpipe and the inside of her lungs, causing permanent damage to her airways.

Lifestyle impact

- Ms Smith has reduced her chances of starting a family.
- Her skin will age faster and her hair will become dull and lank.
- If Ms Smith has asthma she is causing further damage to her airways and has increased her chances of having an asthma attack.
- Her habit could cost her up to £70,000 in a lifetime.

Fatal addiction

- Ms Smith loses at least one day of life each week.
- She is three times more likely to die before retirement.
- She is likely to develop a serious disease such as heart disease, lung cancer, osteoporosis, bronchitis and emphysema.
- She is four times more likely to develop breast cancer.
- She has doubled her risk of dying from coronary heart disease.

NATIONAL **ASTHMA** CAMPAIGN
conquering asthma

- If Ms Smith is also taking oral contraception she has increased her chances of having a heart attack and a stroke.

The passive smoker

Passive smoking is responsible for the death of over 22,000 people each year in Europe. Mr Brown could be one of them. Although he has never smoked himself, a number of his friends – including Ms Smith – do.

Smoking statistics

Information from KATS

- Every day in Great Britain about 450 children start smoking.
- It is very rare for someone to take up smoking as an adult, the majority of smokers start during adolescence.
- 95% of smokers started smoking as children.
- Every day over 300 smokers die as a result of their habit.
- Approximately half of all smokers will ultimately be killed by their habit.
- Tobacco is the only legally available product which, even when used correctly, harms the users.
- 20% of women and 32% of men are ex-smokers.
- 67% of current smokers would like to quit.
- Smoking kills almost six times as many people as road and other accidents, suicide, murder, manslaughter, poisoning, over-doses and HIV put together!

© KATS (Kids against tobacco smoke) – The Roy Castle Lung Cancer Foundation

---

Health warning

- Mr Brown inhales unfiltered smoke containing higher concentrations of the 4,000 toxins contained in a cigarette.
- If Mr Brown is exposed to unfiltered smoke for a long period of time he is more likely to develop a serious disease such as heart disease, lung cancer and bronchitis and emphysema.
- Mr Brown has a 30 per cent increased chance of developing lung cancer. Passive smoking is thought to be responsible for up to 300 deaths from lung cancer each year.
- Being in a smoky room makes Mr Brown's eyes sore and irritates his nose and throat.
- Mr Brown may also experience headaches, dizziness and even nausea.
- If he has asthma, Mr Brown is likely to find that tobacco smoke triggers an asthma attack.

In 1996 a survey by the National Asthma Campaign showed that as many as 80 per cent of the UK's 3.4 million people with asthma say that other people's tobacco smoke makes their symptoms worse.

Smoking and your baby

Whatever your good intentions it can be difficult to give up smoking during pregnancy. But, to give your child the best start in life, it's important to address the facts.

Before the birth

Smoking during pregnancy:

- reduces the amount of oxygen that your baby gets through the umbilical cord. This makes your baby's heart beat faster and your baby grow more slowly.
- reduces the blood flow through the placenta so that your baby gets less nutrients.
- brings a 50 per cent increased risk of your baby developing allergies such as asthma, eczema, hay fever and rhinitis.

- increases the chance of complications during pregnancy including a miscarriage or a premature birth.

After the birth

More than 17,000 children under five are admitted to hospital each year because of the effects of passive smoking. Smoking around your baby:

- doubles the risk of your child dying from cot death.
- increases the risk of your baby developing a serious respiratory disease by 50 per cent.

Breaths of fresh air

What is being done for people with asthma?

The National Asthma Campaign:

- works with other organisations to support initiatives that help to reduce the number of people who smoke in the UK.
- has pressed the Government for a ban on tobacco advertising – to date a new EU directive is set to ban tobacco advertising in 2003.
- is calling for a ban on smoking in public places. We have already encouraged a number of restaurants and other venues to sign a Public Places Charter, indicating whether they have non-smoking areas available.
- has responded to a Government consultation about a new Approved Code of Practice on smoking in the workplace and

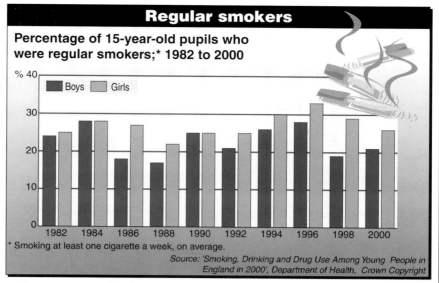

Regular smokers

Percentage of 15-year-old pupils who were regular smokers;* 1982 to 2000

% 40 — Boys / Girls — 1982 1984 1986 1988 1990 1992 1994 1996 1998 2000

* Smoking at least one cigarette a week, on average.

Source: 'Smoking, Drinking and Drug Use Among Young People in England in 2000', Department of Health, Crown Copyright

has encouraged other organisations to join in the campaign to reduce the impact of tobacco smoke in the workplace.

- has supported the implementation of cessation guidelines for health professionals which explain how they can best help smokers who want to quit.

Where can I get help?

- For free advice on how to stop smoking call Quitline on 0800 00 22 00 open 1pm to 9pm seven days a week. Or Pregnancy Quitline 0800 00 22 11.
- For a free booklet *Stopping Smoking Made Easier* telephone the Health Education Authority 020 7413 1900.

Or get on-line at:

www.dontsmoke.com
Offering advice and support to help you give up smoking

www.lifesaver.co.uk
An interactive website offering the support and motivation you may need to quit

www.ash.org.uk
General information about smoking and ways to give up

• This article is an extract from *Asthma News*, January 2000. Reproduced with kind permission of the National Asthma Campaign. See their web site at www.asthma.org.uk or see page 41 for their address details.

© *National Asthma Campaign*

What's in a cigarette

Information from No Smoking Day

Many of us worry about the alarming number of additives, colourings, preservatives and other ingredients that are added to the food we eat. But how many of us are aware that 4,000 chemicals occur naturally in tobacco, some of which are very familiar:

Tar

Tar is a mixture of chemicals (formaldehyde, arsenic and cyanide to name a few) which are drawn into the smoker's lungs when cigarette smoke is inhaled. Once inhaled, the smoke condenses and about 70 per cent of the tar is deposited in the smoker's lungs. Many of the substances in tar are known to cause cancer in animals and they damage the lungs and the small hairs that help protect the lungs from dirt and infection.

Nicotine

Nicotine is a powerful and fast-acting drug, which once absorbed reaches the brain in about seven seconds. Most people who smoke are dependent on the nicotine in cigarettes. After starting to smoke, nicotine increases your heart rate and blood pressure. Other effects of nicotine include an increase in hormone production, the constriction of small blood vessels under the skin and changes in blood composition.

Carbon monoxide (CO)

Carbon monoxide is an odourless, tasteless and poisonous gas, giving no warning of its presence in most circumstances. In large amounts it is rapidly fatal. It is formed when a cigarette is lit. It combines with haemoglobin in the blood more readily than oxygen, so up to 15% of a smoker's blood may be carrying CO instead of oxygen. This makes the heart work harder to pump less oxygen around the body thus making breathing more difficult. This is why CO is linked to coronary heart disease and other circulation problems.

In addition, cigarette smoke is estimated to contain more than 4,000 chemicals including over 40 known cancer-causing substances:

Acetone – widely used as a solvent, for example in nail-polish remover

Ammonia – found in dry-cleaning fluids

Arsenic – a deadly poison, used in insecticides

Formaldehyde – highly poisonous and used to preserve dead bodies

Cadmium – a highly poisonous metal used in batteries

Shellac – when mixed with denatured alcohol, the resin becomes a wood varnish

Benzene – used as a solvent in fuel and chemical manufacturing

Cyanide – a deadly poison

• The above information is an extract from the No Smoking Day web site which can be found at www.nosmokingday.org.uk

Risk factors and determinants of cigarette smoking

Information from the Royal College of Physicians

Gender

The effect of gender on the likelihood of being a smoker is changing. Smoking in Britain has been more common in men for most of this century, but the difference in prevalence between men and women has been decreasing for many years and in 1997 the point estimate of cigarette smoking prevalence was actually slightly higher in women than in men.[1] This estimate did not allow for cigar or pipe smoking, so overall in Britain men are probably more likely than women to be smokers, but the difference between the sexes is now very small.

A trend towards female smoking has been evident for several years amongst schoolchildren, and the gap between the sexes has been increasing.[2] For some time therefore, females have accounted for the majority of young smokers entering the smoking population. Although the future relative prevalence of smoking in young male and female adults will depend on uptake and cessation rates in both sexes during the later teenage years, these data indicate that the proportion of females in the smoking population may be set to increase further.

Age

Age is a major determinant of smoking behaviour. Smoking is very

uncommon in children up to and including the age of 11 years, but increases substantially at 12-15 years old, to the extent that in 1996 28% of boys and 33% of girls were regular smokers by age 15.[2] Amongst adults, smoking prevalence is greatest in the 20-24 age group, thereafter decreasing progressively with age.

Socio-economic status

Smoking behaviour is strongly related to socio-economic status. In relation to occupation in 1996,

smoking prevalence was lowest in the professional (12%) and highest in the semi-skilled manual occupational groups (39%).[2] Data on the trend in smoking prevalence within non-manual and manual occupational groups suggest that the difference between these groups has, if anything, widened in recent years, more so in women. However, other measures of relative poverty or deprivation, including housing tenure, crowding, living in rented accommodation, being divorced or separated, unemployment, low educational achievement, and in women, single parent status, are also independently associated with an increased risk of smoking amongst adults.[3] Analysis of trends in smoking

based on a composite index of some of these measures indicates that over the period 1973-1996 smoking prevalence fell by more than 50% in the most advantaged sector of British society, but has remained unchanged in the most deprived group.[3] Similar findings apply to smoking cessation rates, which also show a strong inverse relation with deprivation. Cessation rates have doubled in the most advantaged groups, but have remained almost unchanged over the past two decades in the most disadvantaged sectors of society.[4]

Region of residence

Smoking prevalence varies in the regions. Data for NHS Regional Office areas of England reveal that the highest prevalence is in the North West Region (30%) and the lowest in the South and West Region (25%).[2]

Risk factors for smoking in children

The factors associated with smoking in children broadly reflect those established for adults. Recent survey data[5] from children aged 11-15 years in England identify several factors associated with the likelihood of smoking in children, including:

- low educational achievement: children who are planning to take GCSE examinations, but with an expectation of passing in fewer than five subjects, are more than twice as likely to be smokers (26%) than those with higher expectations (10%);
- living with parents who smoke: children living with two parents who both smoke are nearly three times as likely to be smokers than those whose parents do not smoke, an effect particularly marked in girls;
- having siblings who smoke: children who have at least one sibling who smokes are four times more likely to smoke (26%) than those with no siblings who smoke (6%).

The following have been identified as additional potential risk factors:
- low socio-economic status
- having friends who smoke
- having teachers who smoke.[6]

References
1 Freeth S. *Smoking-related behaviour and attitudes, 1997.* A report on research using the Omnibus Survey produced on behalf of the Department of Health. London: Office for National Statistics, 1998.
2 *Statistics on smoking: England, 1976 to 1996.* Department of Health Bulletin 1998/25. London: Department of Health, 1998.
3 Jarvis MJ, Wardle J. Social patterning of individual health behaviours: the case of cigarette smoking. In: Marmot M, Wilkinson R (eds). *Social determinants of health.* Oxford: Oxford University Press, 1999: 240-55.
4 Jarvis MJ. Patterns and predictors of smoking cessation in the general population. In: Bolliger CT, Fagerström KO (eds). *The tobacco epidemic.* Basel: Karger, 1997: 151-64.
5 Barton J. *Young teenagers and smoking in 1997.* London: Health Education Authority, 1998.
6 *Smoking and the young.* A report of a working party of the Royal College of Physicians. London: RCP, 1992.

• The above information is an extract from *Nicotine Addiction in Britain*, a report of the Tobacco Advisory Group of the Royal College of Physicians, London 2000. Visit their web site at www.rcplondon.ac.uk

Young people and smoking

Smoking prevalence

Children become aware of cigarettes at an early age. Three out of four children are aware of cigarettes before they reach the age of 5 whether the parents smoke or not.[1] By the age of 11 one-third of children, and by 16 years two-thirds of children have experimented with smoking.[2] In Great Britain about 450 children start smoking every day.[3] Large regional studies of children's smoking habits during the 1960s and 1970s showed that more boys smoked than girls and that boys started earlier.[4] In 1982, at ASH's instigation, the government commissioned the first national survey of smoking among children and found that 11% of 11-16-year-olds were smoking regularly.[5]

During the early nineties prevalence remained stable at 10%, but by the mid-nineties teenage smoking rates were on the increase, particularly among girls. Between 1996 and 1999, there was a decline in 11-15-year-olds smoking regularly.[6] The reduction in smoking prevalence occurred mainly among 14-15-year-olds. The proportion of regular smokers increases sharply with age: the 1999 study found that 3% of 12-year-olds, 12% of 14-year-olds and 23% of 15-year-olds were regular smokers. The latest survey has revealed a slight increase in overall prevalence but because of the fluctuation in teenage smoking behaviour since the early 1980s, it is not possible to say whether this is the beginning of a new upward trend in smoking.[7]

References
1 *Teenage Smoking attitudes in 1996.* Office for National Statistics, 1997
2 *Drug use, smoking and drinking among young teenagers in 1999.* National Statistics, 2000.
3 *Smoking and the Young.* Royal College of Physicians. London, RCP, 1992.
4 Bewley B.R., Day I., Ide L. *Smoking by children in Great Britain.* MRC Social Science Research Council, 1972.
5 Dobbs J., Marsh A. *Smoking among secondary schoolchildren.* HMSO, 1982.
6 *Drug use, smoking and drinking among young teenagers in 1999.* National Statistics, 2000.
7 *Smoking, drinking and drug use among young people in England in 2000.* Department of Health press release, 26/7/01

• The above information is an extract from an Action on Smoking and Health (ASH) factsheet *Young People and Smoking* which can be viewed on their web site at www.ash.org.uk

Hard facts

Young people and smoking

A cool habit?
- One person dies from a smoking-related disease every 4 minutes in Britain. That's the same as a full Jumbo Jet crashing every single day for a year
- Most people killed by tobacco started smoking when they were teenagers
- Around half of the teenagers who carry on smoking will eventually be killed by tobacco. Half of these will die in middle age (between 35 and 69)

. . . does that sound cool to you?
From the moment you stop smoking your life gets better . . .

Young people often start smoking because they think it's glamorous and grown up, and don't think that they'll be smoking for life. But don't underestimate the addictive nature of nicotine. It's not like shopping or chocolate – nicotine is as addictive as heroin and cocaine. Seventy per cent of adult smokers started when they were aged 11-15 – do you think they all thought they'd carry on for so long? Stopping smoking is not easy and the best solution is never to start in the first place.

The facts

Save your life
Smoking contributes to cancer, heart disease, bronchitis, strokes, stomach ulcers, leukaemia, gum disease, gangrene, asthma, wrinkles, bad breath . . .

Keep fit
Smoking makes you short of breath, making sport and exercise more difficult.

Passive smoking
Breathing in other people's smoke is called passive smoking. This can cause headaches and lack of concentration. Each year around 17,000 kids under the age of 5 go into hospital with complaints caused by smoke from their parents' cigarettes.

You care
Children as young as 5 years old have tried cigarettes. Kids are more likely to try smoking if they have seen their brothers or sisters doing it. So be a positive role model and influence on your family – don't smoke.

The myths

It helps me unwind
Cigarettes don't make you relax. Nicotine is a stimulant. It actually speeds up your bodily functions – especially your heart rate.

Do you think I'm sexy?
Kissing someone with a mouth like an ashtray isn't sexy. Having smoke blown in your face isn't sexy. Lung cancer isn't sexy. However buying someone special a gift with the money you didn't spend on smoking is definitely sexy.

Shape shifter
If you think you'll put on weight if you stop smoking, then think again. Cigarettes don't keep your body weight down and they can even cause cellulite. Some people replace cigarettes with food when they give up therefore may put on a few pounds. But if you've managed to give up smoking, you'll be able to tackle any weight gain, without any problems.

Something to do with your friends
So you want to while away the time with your friends by killing yourself? If you like you could also try and get run over by a bus. Alternatively, there are plenty of other more body-friendly and exciting things to do: try out a new sport, go and see a movie, listen to your favourite music, start a band, read the latest bestseller.

I'm independent; I can smoke if I want to
Smoking is addictive, and being an addict makes you more dependent than independent.

It makes me look mature
Only in the sense that smoking gives you wrinkles before your time. There's nothing mature about smelling like an ashtray and inhaling vast amounts of grim chemicals.

Saying 'No' . . .
Real friends will respect your right to make up your own mind. But if you're not sure how to say no, here are some suggestions . . .
- 'I'm not sure what cigarette-stained fingers, smelly clothes and hair and yellow teeth would do to my fabulous rating'

The real cost of smoking

Smokers know only too well the expense of buying cigarettes. In fact, 20-a-day smokers will spend more than £1,300 a year on their habit.

As well as the cost of cigarettes, lighting up in some places can result in big fines:
- Up to £1,000 if you smoke on a bus
- Up to £1,000 if you light up on the Underground
- Up to £2,500 if you smoke on a non-smoking flight – more if the flight is delayed or diverted
- Like any other litter, you can be fined £25 for dropping a cigarette butt in Westminster
- Up to £50 for lighting up on a Virgin or Central train.

But: If you gave up a 20-a-day habit at the age of 20 and invested that money in a pension fund you'd have nearly £1 million to retire with at age 60.

- No Smoking Day provides practical help and support for smokers who want to quit. Research shows that around two-thirds of smokers do want to quit but many need added support and encouragement to help them succeed. Each year over a million people take part in No Smoking Day and an estimated 40,000 quit.

© No Smoking Day

- 'Blowing chemical-ridden smoke over my best mate is not the way I show I care'
- 'Not just at the moment. When I want to shorten my life a little I'll give you a call'
- 'Not for me. If I want to avoid pulling sometime though, I'll let you know'

In the media

Research shows that the top cigarette brands smoked by children are also the ones most heavily advertised.

Legislation drastically curbing the promotion of cigarette sales is being debated by MPs. And the European Parliament is keen to toughen health warnings on cigarette packets. We can expect to see new legislation that will increase health warnings to 30% of the front and 60% of the back of packets. At the moment, they occupy 4% of the packaging in Europe. In the USA the proportion is 6% and in Canada it is 50%.

What do you think about the advertising of cigarettes?

Interesting web sites

Lifebytes
Health facts for 11-14-year-olds: www.lifebytes.gov.uk

Mind, Body, Soul
Health facts for 14-16-year-olds: www.mindbodysoul.gov.uk

QuitNow Australia
Not for the faint-hearted – gory pictures of what smoking does to various organs: www.quitnow.info.au

Florida Truth Campaign
Reveals the truth behind US tobacco manufacturers: www.wholetruth.com

- The above information is an extract from the Department of Health web site www.givingupsmoking.co.uk
© Crown Copyright

Children and smoking

Information from the Tobacco Manufacturers' Association (TMA)

The UK tobacco companies are against children smoking and have for many years initiated campaigns aimed at preventing children from buying cigarettes (e.g. Greenfinch, No Excuses, CitizenCard®).

Tobacco companies' advertising and marketing are aimed at the adult smoker and they comply with a wide range of tough regulations to prevent children being exposed to advertising of tobacco products.

Parents and society as a whole have a part to play in preventing children from smoking – it is not just up to tobacco manufacturers and retailers.

Children should not smoke. When they become adults, they should be free to make up their own minds about smoking – just like any other legal activity.

- It has been illegal to sell tobacco products to a child under 16 years of age since 1908.[1] The companies are in favour of a government-backed proof-of-age card to reinforce retailers' efforts to prevent under-age purchase.
- CitizenCard®, a national proof-of-age scheme, was launched in February 1999.
  – It aims to prevent young people from purchasing cigarettes, alcohol and other age-restricted products while under the legal age.

TOBACCO
Manufacturers' Association

– It is a non-profit scheme backed by the Association of Convenience Stores, Camelot, Ladbrokes, the National Federation of Retail Newsagents, Somerfield Stores and the Tobacco Manufacturers' Association, with the support of the Government.
– Over 32,000 cards were sold in its first year and CitizenCard® made the card free to all 16- and 17-year-olds from the autumn of 2000. By the end of April 2001, over 100,000 cards had been issued.
– A schools pack to encourage good citizenship was developed by CitizenCard® for distribution to schools in September 2000.
- The TMA believes that tobacco advertising is not one of the determining factors in whether children start smoking. A view backed up by a 1998 critical review of the literature examining the psychological factors related to adolescent smoking by Tyas and Pederson as detailed in the *Nursing Standard* 26 September 2001, page 39.

Legal age

- Deciding on the legal age at which tobacco products may be purchased is up to the Government. At present, the legal age of 'adulthood' seems inconsistent. The tobacco industry will comply with any change of UK legislation.
- Simply raising the legal age of purchase will not have any effect unless there is a nationally recognised, Government-backed proof-of-age scheme to back up the retailer in refusing to sell to children.
- Eliminating uncontrolled sales of cheap, illegally imported cigarettes would help discourage availability to under-age purchasers.
- While there should be stiff penalties for retailers who knowingly infringe the law, it is not fair to put all the blame on retailers when it is so difficult to prove a young person's age. It is far more effective to motivate them and help them avoid doing so by making use of proof-of-age cards far more widespread.

Reference
1 Children's Act 1908

- The above information is an extract from the Tobacco Manufacturers' Association web site which can be found at www.the-tma.org.uk
© Tobacco Manufacturers' Association (TMA)

Film icons blamed for teenage smoking

*By Sarah Boseley,
Health Editor*

Film stars such as Leonardo Di-Caprio, Sharon Stone and John Travolta who regularly smoke on screen are influencing young people to take up cigarettes, according to a study.

Psychologists from the United States believe they have concrete evidence that young fans are swayed by the image of their idol with a cigarette between their fingers.

While they accept there are limitations to their study, Jennifer Tickle and her colleagues from New Hampshire said their research found a surprisingly strong link between use by movie stars of tobacco and higher levels of smoking in the teenagers who admire them.

On the strength of the findings, the smoking pressure group Action on Smoking and Health (Ash) is asking the British Board of Film Classification not to give less than a 15 certificate to a film showing teen idols smoking.

Clive Bates, director of Ash, said: 'We don't want to censor directors and actors by banning smoking in films by law, but we do call on them to think about harm they are doing.

'Hollywood megastars can find the best support in the world to stop smoking if they want, but for young fans the influence of their favourite actors could be the start of a lifetime struggle with nicotine addiction.'

The questionnaire, in the medical journal *Tobacco Control* published today, featured 632 students, aged between 10 and 19, from five rural New England schools. They were asked about their tobacco use and also the name of their favourite film star. The psychologists then analysed the smoking patterns in recent films of the 43 most popular stars. They found that 65% smoked on screen at least once and 42% portrayed smoking as an essential character trait in one or more films. Three film stars – Leonardo DiCaprio, Sharon Stone and John Travolta – smoked in three or more films.

They found that those teenagers who named a favourite film star who had smoked on screen were more likely to smoke or say they were inclined to smoke. And the more their film idol smoked on screen, the higher the chance that the young person would be a smoker.

> **Teenagers who named a favourite film star who had smoked on screen were more likely to smoke or say they were inclined to smoke**

'This research shows a clear relation between on-screen tobacco use by movie stars and higher levels of smoking uptake in the adolescents who admire them,' said the researchers. They added that there was no evidence that teenagers who already smoked were more interested in the characters who smoked in the films they watched.

'Instead the association between star smoking and attitudes that predict smoking (susceptibility) was even stronger among never smokers, suggesting that the influence of movie star smoking begins before experimentation with cigarettes. We believe this evidence strongly suggests that media portrayals of tobacco use by popular movie stars contribute to adolescent smoking.'

They accept that adolescents may admire film stars who smoke because it fits their pre-existing concept of 'cool' behaviour.

The results of the study, said the authors, 'contribute to a growing body of evidence identifying media exposure to smoking as a major contributing factor in adolescent smoking uptake'.

School lets its pupils smoke

By Richard Alleyne

A school has become the first in Britain to allow pupils to smoke in the playground.

Pupils at Greenhill Special School, Cardiff, South Wales, have been told they can smoke during breaks provided their parents agree. The policy has been introduced at the school, for children aged 11 to 16 with emotional and behavioural difficulties, in an attempt to maintain discipline.

A spokesman for Ash, the anti-smoking pressure group, criticised the school for condoning smoking. 'We are absolutely shocked and cannot see the rationale behind this. We are surprised that a school would condone such behaviour.' A spokesman for the Department of Health said the step was very unusual. 'We expect schools to pursue health education, but at the very last resort it's up to the schools.'

A spokesman for Cardiff county council said Greenhill Special School was a unique case. 'There are 52,000 pupils in Cardiff schools and there is a no-smoking policy in all of them except Greenhill. Because it has severe behavioural problems this decision was taken, with parental consent, to help run the school smoothly.'

Smokers' rights declaration

In keeping with, and based upon, the United Nations Universal Declaration of Human Rights, adopted 1948, herewith is the Smokers' Declaration of Rights*

Preamble

Whereas recognition of the inherent dignity and of the equal and inalienable rights of all members of the human family is the foundation of freedom, justice and peace in the world, Whereas smokers are considered human beings as well, Whereas it is essential for smokers to rebel against tyranny and oppression.

Article 1

The Right to be equal in dignity and rights.

Article 2

The Right to be considered as a group of people covered under the United Nations Universal Declaration of Human Rights.

Article 3

The Right to life, liberty and security of person while exercising our choice to smoke.

Article 4

The Right to be free from being subjected to cruel, inhuman, degrading treatment and punishment.[1]

Article 5

The Right not to be treated as, and considered to be, second-class citizens.

Article 6

The Right not to be discriminated against in the workplace, in housing, in employment opportunities, in establishments, in adoption of children, in the raising and keeping of their own children.[2]

Article 7

The Right not to be forced into arbitrary exile from establishments, housing, employment, and public buildings.

Article 8

The Right to be included as active participants and voters in fair and public hearings as regards to where a human being may or may not smoke.

Article 9

The Right to be active, essential, and

October 12th

World Smoker's Day

voting part to all debates, policies, legal and administrative procedures concerning the taxation, limitation, regulation of our persons and lifestyle, and to all processes that otherwise economically and politically affect the exercise of our right to smoke.

Article 10

The Right to be accused of being responsible for harming others with our tobacco smoke by state and institutions only after unbiased, transparent, verifiable, and scientifically unquestionable evidence has proven beyond any reasonable doubt that second-hand smoke is harmful to third parties.

Article 11

The Right to be accused of being responsible for harming ourselves with our tobacco smoke by state and institutions only after transparent, verifiable, and scientifically un-

questionable evidence has proven beyond any reasonable doubt that smoking is responsible for the specific diseases attributed to it, and beyond the effects of confounders.

Article 12

The Right to be free from arbitrary interference in privacy, family, home and activities by state and institutions; and the Right to preserve honour and reputation as smokers.

Article 13

The Right to travel as comfortably as non-smokers do, on any means of transportation.

Article 14

The Right to leave or enter any country, without discrimination or persecution based on our choice, in conjunction with the right to exercise our choice to smoke.

Article 15

The Right to not have our families be torn asunder based solely on whether or not a resident adult smokes.[3]

Article 16

The Right not to be deprived from our property – as it is the case for smoking prisoners, whose tobacco products are routinely confiscated.

Article 17

The Right to freely, publicly, and equitably speak out against hatred, bigotry, and discrimination being perpetrated against people who smoke.

Article 18

The Right to demand equal time for the rebuttal of false, distorted, misleading and slanderous information against smokers and smoking perpetrated by state, media, and institutions against those who have chosen to smoke.

Article 19

The Right to use legal and political procedures when state and institutions divulge unverified, misleading, slanderous, or otherwise inaccurate information on tobacco products, the choice and the habit of smoking, and the effects of smoking, for the purpose of creating hostile and discriminatory environments against smokers, as well as attempting to influence the choice of smoking through libellous and inaccurate information.[4]

Article 20

The Right to peaceful assembly and associate with other smokers and/or their supporters while exercising their choice to smoke.

Article 21

The Right to work, and to freely and unrestrictedly choose employment, and to favourable conditions of work while exercising our choice to smoke; to be selected as workers, free from prejudice and discrimination about our smoking lifestyle choice; to be entitled to the same protection against unemployment applicable to those who do not smoke.

Article 22

The Right to enjoy rest and leisure as we see fit while exercising our choice to smoke.

Article 23

The Right to enjoy medical care and social services free of the prejudice, discrimination, restrictions, coercion, overcharge, paternalism, propaganda against (and misinformation on) smoking now perpetrated by state and health establishment against smokers.

Article 24

The Right to receive respect for human rights and fundamental freedoms, understanding, tolerance, and friendship.[5]

Article 25

The Right to freely participate in the cultural life of the community, even when that community is comprised of smokers and their supporters.

Article 26

The Right to a social and international order in which the rights and freedoms set forth in the United Nations Universal Declaration of Human Rights can be fully realised for all.

Article 27

The Right to exercise our rights and freedoms as regards the just requirements of morality, public order, and the general welfare in a democratic society.[6]

Article 28

The Right to expect that the Smokers' Rights are unalienable, and therefore they shall not be destroyed, endangered, limited.

Notes

* Although the United Nations no longer seems to believe in, or abide by, their own Declaration of Human Rights, smokers are here to remind them that at least one segment of global society still take their Articles seriously.

1 The removal of children from their homes; refusal of employment or housing; denial of medical treatment; being forced to smoke outdoors, in all weather conditions; cruel, degrading, hateful, and bigoted comments from strangers.

2 Many organisations encourage, condone, and incite these discriminatory activities against smokers.

3 Smokers are increasingly, and systematically, being refused employment and favourable work conditions.

4 For example, the mandatory printing of propaganda and inaccurate information on the effects of smoking on cigarette packets.

5 Being treated as second-class citizens and pariahs even by family members, solely because of smoking is disrespectful and intolerant.

6 Consistently, smokers have been banned from the 'democratic process' which prevents smokers from engaging in a legal, pleasurable activity. This is highly immoral.

• The above information is from the World Smokers' Day web site: www.worldsmokersday.org

© FORCES International

The basic smoking debate facts and figures

The UK £9.5 billion smoker's 'sin' tax is equivalent to approximately 22% of expenditure on health, 26% of expenditure on education and 52% of expenditure on defence (for the fiscal year 2000/2001).

The UK Treasury is currently losing £1 billion a year as a result of legitimate cross-border purchasing and £3.8 billion due to illegal smuggling of tobacco products because British tobacco taxes are among the highest in Europe. Further increases in tobacco tax are likely to result in a greater loss of revenue.

The taxation on a pack of cigarettes bought in the UK amounts to about 79% of the total price. Some low price brands can have a tax element of 90%.

There are 15 million smokers in the UK. There were 10.7 million people who voted Labour in the 2001 General Election. So: 'More Smokers than Labour Voters!'

• The above information is an extract from FOREST's web site which can be found at www.forest-on-smoking.org.uk

© FOREST

Smoking affects everyone . . .

. . . the dangers of passive smoking

Smoking doesn't just affect you. It is estimated that as many as 12,000 cases of heart disease in the UK each year are attributable to passive smoking.* Those particularly at risk are likely to be those closest to you – your children, your family and your friends. Children whose parents smoke are at a higher risk of cot death, asthma and other respiratory diseases, glue ear and, in the long term, are more likely to become smokers themselves. In fact, more than 17,000 children under the age of five are admitted to hospital every year because of the effects of passive smoking.

How passive smoking occurs . . .
- Passive smoking occurs when the non-smoker breathes in 'side-stream' smoke from the burning end of a cigarette and 'main-stream' smoke, which has been inhaled and then exhaled by the smoker
- Non-smokers who breathe other people's tobacco smoke are exposed to the same 4,000 chemicals that a smoker inhales

Who is affected and how . . .
- Children exposed to second-hand smoke are twice as likely to get chest illnesses such as croup, pneumonia bronchitis and bronchiolitis
- Children exposed to second-hand smoke are also more likely to get ear infections, tonsillitis, wheezing and childhood asthma
- Children of smokers are more likely to smoke themselves
- According to government statistics, half of British children live in households where at least one parent smokes
- Non-smokers exposed to second-hand smoke are put at risk of the same serious diseases as smokers
- Cigarette smoke is classified as a cause of cancer

Children whose parents smoke are at a higher risk of cot death, asthma and other respiratory diseases, glue ear and, in the long term, are more likely to become smokers themselves

---

Protecting the public . . .
Smoking is now banned from many public places, including public transport, theatres, cinemas and public buildings, and it is expected that this list will continue to grow. Imagine if smoking became such a social stigma, that the only place where it was acceptable was your home, and quite possibly even there you'd be putting someone else at risk.

If you're affected . . .
Smoking affects everyone. Your decision to smoke is not just about you. It's about those around you.

For more information about the affects of passive smoking, see the Action on Smoking & Health website at www.ash.org.uk

* Figures calculated by ASH based on findings of the Californian Environmental Protection Agency report that shows how many people are affected by passive smoking in California and the USA.

• The above information is an extract from the Department of Health web site www.givingupsmoking.co.uk

© Crown Copyright

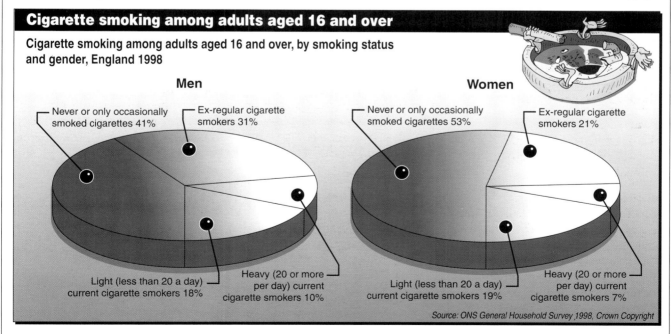

Cigarette smoking among adults aged 16 and over

Cigarette smoking among adults aged 16 and over, by smoking status and gender, England 1998

Men
- Never or only occasionally smoked cigarettes 41%
- Ex-regular cigarette smokers 31%
- Light (less than 20 a day) current cigarette smokers 18%
- Heavy (20 or more per day) current cigarette smokers 10%

Women
- Never or only occasionally smoked cigarettes 53%
- Ex-regular cigarette smokers 21%
- Light (less than 20 a day) current cigarette smokers 19%
- Heavy (20 or more per day) current cigarette smokers 7%

Source: ONS General Household Survey ,1998, Crown Copyright

Passive smoking

Information from ASH

Introduction

Breathing other people's smoke is called passive, involuntary or second-hand smoking. The non-smoker breathes 'sidestream' smoke from the burning tip of the cigarette and 'mainstream' smoke that has been inhaled and then exhaled by the smoker. Environmental tobacco smoke (ETS) is a major source of indoor air pollution.

What's in the smoke?

Tobacco smoke contains over 4000 chemicals in the form of particles and gases.[1] Many potentially toxic gases are present in higher concentrations in sidestream smoke than in mainstream smoke and nearly 85% of the smoke in a room results from sidestream smoke.[2] The particulate phase includes tar (itself composed of many chemicals), nicotine, benzene and benzo(a)pyrene. The gas phase includes carbon monoxide, ammonia, dimethylnitrosamine, formaldehyde, hydrogen cyanide and acrolein. Some of these have marked irritant properties and some 60 are known or suspected carcinogens (cancer causing substances). The Environmental Protection Agency (EPA) in the USA has classified environmental tobacco smoke as a class A (known human) carcinogen along with asbestos, arsenic, benzene and radon gas.[1]

How does this affect the passive smoker?

Some of the immediate effects of passive smoking include eye irritation, headache, cough, sore throat, dizziness and nausea. Adults with asthma can experience a significant decline in lung function when exposed, while new cases of asthma may be induced in children whose parents smoke. Short-term exposure to tobacco smoke also has a measurable effect on the heart in non-smokers. Just 30 minutes' exposure is enough to reduce coronary blood flow.[3]

![ash. action on smoking and health]

In the longer term, passive smokers suffer an increased risk of a range of smoking-related diseases. Non-smokers who are exposed to passive smoking in the home, have a 25% increased risk of heart disease and lung cancer.[4] A major review by the Government-appointed Scientific Committee on Tobacco and Health (SCOTH) concluded that passive smoking is a cause of lung cancer and ischaemic heart disease in adult non-smokers, and a cause of respiratory disease, cot death, middle ear disease and asthmatic attacks in children.[5] While the relative health risks from passive smoking are small in comparison with those from active smoking, because the diseases are common, the overall health impact is large. Based on the findings of the SCOTH report and the review by the California Environmental Protection Agency[10] ASH has calculated that, each year in the UK, about 600 lung cancer deaths and up to 12,000 cases of heart disease in non-smokers can be attributed to passive smoking.[6] (See also ASH's briefing on the health impacts of passive smoking.)

Risk to young children

Almost half of all children in the UK are exposed to tobacco smoke at home.[7] Passive smoking increases the risk of lower respiratory tract infections such as bronchitis, pneumonia and bronchiolitis in children. One study found that in households where both parents smoke, young children have a 72% increased risk of respiratory illnesses.[8] Passive smoking causes a reduction in lung function and increased severity in the symptoms of asthma in children, and is a risk factor for new cases of asthma in children.[9,10] Passive smoking is also associated with middle ear infection in children as well as possible cardiovascular impairment and behavioural problems.[11]

Infants of parents who smoke are more likely to be admitted to hospital for bronchitis and pneumonia in the first year of life. More than 17,000 children under the age of five are admitted to hospital every year because of the effects of passive smoking.[12] Passive smoking during childhood predisposes children to developing chronic obstructive airway disease and cancer as adults.[12]

Exposure to passive smoking during pregnancy is an independent risk factor for low birth weight.[13] A recent study has also shown that babies exposed to their mother's tobacco smoke before they are born grow up with reduced lung function.[14] Parental smoking is also a risk factor for sudden infant death syndrome (cot death).

What protection is there for non-smokers?

A report by the Independent Scientific Committee on Smoking and Health (SCOTH)[5] reviewed the evidence on passive smoking and concluded that: 'Smoking in public places should be restricted on the grounds of public health.' The report added that 'Wherever possible, smoking should not be allowed in the workplace.' Public opinion surveys have shown widespread support for smoking restrictions in public places. A national survey in 1999 found that 85% of respondents (including 71% of smokers) agreed that smoking should be restricted at work and a similar proportion favoured smoking restrictions in restaurants and other public places.[15]

In December 1998, the Government published a White Paper on tobacco which included proposals to tackle the problem of smoking in public places and the workplace.[16] With regard to public places, the Government launched a Public Places charter in conjunction with the hospitality industry. This is designed to increase smoke-free provision in pubs, restaurants, etc. Trade associations that have signed the charter acknowledge that 'non-smoking is the general norm' and are encouraging their members to improve ventilation, have a clear smoking policy and to communicate the policy through appropriate signage.[17]

A survey by ASH in April 1999 revealed that about 3 million people in the UK are exposed to passive smoking in their places of work. In July 1999, the Health and Safety Commission issued a draft Approved Code of Practice to clarify the implementation of the Health & Safety at Work Act as it applies to passive smoking in the workplace. The Act states that employers have a duty 'to provide and maintain a safe working environment which is, so far as is reasonably practicable, safe, without risks to health and adequate as regards facilities and arrangements for their welfare at work'. A legal opinion, commissioned by ASH in 1997, argued that the existing law could be interpreted as requiring employers to provide a smoke-free workplace. For more information on all aspects of smoking in the workplace, see the ASH guide at http://www.ash.org.uk/html/workplace.html

References
1 *Respiratory health effects of passive smoking.* EPA/600/6-90/006F United States Environmental Protection Agency, 1992.
2 Fielding, JE and Phenow, KJ. *New England J. of Medicine* 1988; 319: 1452-60.
3 Otsuka, R. Acute effects of passive smoking on the coronary circulation in healthy young adults. *JAMA* 2001; 286: 436-441 .

Some of the immediate effects of passive smoking include eye irritation, headache, cough, sore throat, dizziness and nausea

---

4 Law, MR et al. Environmental tobacco smoke exposure and ischaemic heart disease: an evaluation of the evidence. *BMJ* 1997; 315: 973-80. Hackshaw AK et al. The accumulated evidence on lung cancer and environmental tobacco smoke. *BMJ* 1997; 315: 980-88.
5 *Report of the Scientific Committee on Tobacco and Health.* Department of Health, 1998.
6 *Passive smoking.* ASH, January 2000
7 *General Household Survey 1998,* Office for National Statistics, 1999.
8 Strachan, DP and Cook, DG. Parental smoking and lower respiratory illness in infancy and early childhood. *Thorax* 1997; 52: 905-914.
9 *Respiratory health effects of passive smoking.* EPA/600/6-90/006F United States Environmental Protection Agency, 1992.
10 Health effects of exposure to environmental tobacco smoke. *Report of the California EPA.* NCI, 1999.
11 *International Consultation on ETS and Child Health.* WHO/NCD/TFI/99.10, World Health Organisation, 1999.
12 *Smoking and the Young.* Royal College of Physicians, 1992.
13 Health effects of exposure to environmental tobacco smoke. The report of the California Environmental Protection Agency. *Smoking and Tobacco Control Monograph 10,* National Cancer Institute, 1999.
14 Gilliland, FD et al. *Thorax* 2000; 55: 271-276
15 Lader, D and Meltzer, H. *Smoking related behaviour and attitudes,* 1999. ONS, 2000.
16 *Smoking Kills. A White Paper on Tobacco.* The Stationery Office, 1998.
17 *A guide to the public places charter on smoking.* Association of Licensed Multiple Retailers, 1999.

• The above information is an extract from a factsheet produced by ASH. Copies of this and other factsheets are available on their web site which can be found at www.ash.org.uk Alternatively see page 41 for their address details.

© ASH – Action on Smoking and Health

The truth about 'passive smoking'

Information from FOREST

In February 2000 a remarkable report was published in the *British Medical Journal* which injected some much needed perspective into the subject of passive smoking. After investigating the issue, researchers at Warwick University had concluded that the risk to non-smokers from exposure to other people's tobacco smoke is not only over-stated but has been wilfully distorted by the anti-smoking lobby.

Risk of passive smoking greatly exaggerated

The study, published in the *British Medical Journal* on 12th February 2000, found that the anti-smoker industry has deliberately inflated the risks and has dismissed research that doesn't support its preconceived ideas. It explained that the level of risk of non-smokers developing lung cancer due to passive smoking (based on 37 studies) is highly suspect because a further 23 studies which failed to link passive smoking with lung cancer were ignored.

Such bias arises because, while studies with positive (and therefore newsworthy) results are likely to be published by medical or scientific journals, those with negative results are not. When reviewers analyse the available data they are not taking into account the unpublished results and the overall picture is therefore distorted.

After factoring for publication bias, the Warwick team concluded that the increased risk of lung cancer from exposure to other people's smoke is more likely to be around 15 as opposed to 24 per cent. Dr Theodore Dalrymple has put such risks in perspective when he wrote,

'The chances of a non-smoker contracting lung cancer are very small indeed, and a fraction . . . of a small risk is not itself a large risk'

(*Sunday Telegraph*, 16th November 1998).

The Warwick report was no surprise to those of us who have been watching the anti-smoking industry in action. In 1992 the American Environmental Protection Agency published a report that was said to prove the link between passive smoking and ill health in non-smokers, yet in 1998 a federal court ruled that the EPA had completely failed to prove its case

In 1997 an Australian Federal Court judge ruled that the (Australian) National Health and Medical Research Council had similarly acted improperly in preparing its report on passive smoking. Further, in March 1998, the World Health Organisation was forced to admit, in a press release, that the results of a seven-year study (the largest of its kind) into the link between passive smoking and lung cancer were not 'statistically significant'.

A year later, in July 1999, in its draft Approved Code of Practice on Smoking at Work, the United Kingdom's Health and Safety Commission stated that:

'Proving beyond reasonable doubt that passive smoking . . . was a risk to health is likely to be very difficult, given the state of the scientific evidence.'

The truth of this statement is undeniable. We often hear that

employers risk being taken to court by employees suffering from 'passive smoking'. In fact, only two 'passive smoking' cases have ever come to court in the UK, and on each occasion the plaintiff has lost. The first to reach a British court was that of Agnes Rae v Glasgow City Council in March 1997, where the plaintiff claimed that exposure to workplace 'passive smoking' had damaged her health. To support the claim that environmental tobacco smoke (ETS) was a danger to health, the pursuer cited a series of reports from various medical and non-medical bodies.

In passing judgement Lord Bonomy said that nowhere was any proof offered 'that any of these statements or indeed the documents from which they are taken identified a risk of lung or respiratory disease being contracted at work as a result of passive smoking ... It follows that there is no averment of when and how the defenders ought to have known of such a risk.'

The second case took place in the High Court in Manchester in March 1998. In Sylvia Sparrow v St Andrews Homes, Mrs Sparrow alleged that being exposed to smokers in the workplace had caused her to become asthmatic. However, Justice Holland rejected her claims and ruled that the employers had done everything practical to accommodate her dislike of tobacco smoke. In his judgement Justice Holland stated that the medical evidence on the link between asthma and ETS exposure was, at best, modest. In addition, witnesses for both the plaintiff and the defendant agreed that 'there had been little research into a possible connection between passive smoking and late onset of asthma in adults'.

Wanted: a victim

It is easy to see why the focus of the smoking debate has shifted from the dangers of primary smoking to the idea that smokers are a danger to non-smokers. A victim was necessary, and one was duly found – the 'passive smoker'. The first of these unfortunates seems to have been a mouse. It was, however, not a very convincing victim, for E Lorenze et al (Cancer Research 3 [2]: 1943) found no evidence of harm done to mice exposed to cigarette smoke for up to 693 hours.

The expression 'passive smoking' was first used in Germany when in 1963 an article by H Otto in the Frankfurter Zeitschrift für Pathologie was entitled 'Experimentelle Untersuchungen an Maeusen mit passiver Zigarettenrauch-beatmung'. It was not, however, until 1975, when the World Health Organisation (WHO) organised the Third World Conference on Smoking and Health that the subject gained popularity. A delegate cited the case of one patient who, while working in an area where smoking was allowed, 'became so tight with wheezing and asthma that she could not get her breath'.

'Proving beyond reasonable doubt that passive smoking . . . was a risk to health is likely to be very difficult, given the state of the scientific evidence'

From this one case, for which he did not give any medical evidence, the delegate drew a picture of approximately 34 million others for whom the problem is real and extremely serious. He gave no evidence for this apart from quoting information on carbon dioxide supplied by a researcher whose conclusions on passive smoking had already been questioned by two American government agencies.

Twenty-six years later environmental tobacco smoke has still not been proved to be an allergen – that is, capable of causing allergic reactions. Yet at another conference in 1979 two researchers referred to a report showing that Swedish asthmatic patients had a positive (bad) reaction to skin testing with tobacco leaf extract. This is not the same as breathing tobacco smoke. There are no doubt many plants that, mixed up and applied to the skin, would prove irritating, a fact emphasised in an article entitled 'Tobacco Allergy – Does it Exist?' in Laekatidningen, 1980.

In America researchers reported on discomfort felt by asthmatics exposed to very high levels of smoke, levels which were recognised as unrealistic even by the researchers. They didn't do what is usual in such studies – find non-asthmatics who could be similarly tested, to compare the effects. Two more researchers reported that they had found non-smokers exposed to smoking (unspecified) in their workplaces for 20 years who had 'lower values of small-airways function'. However, critics pointed out that there was no evidence that this meant anything at all, or did anyone any harm, and questioned where the researchers had found a typical group of workers who had never been exposed to smoke for 20 years for the necessary comparison. Four more studies showed no relationship between passive smoking and respiratory disease.

Curiously, smoking in the UK has fallen from over half the population in 1970 to below 30 per cent today during which time the number of asthma cases has doubled. This discrepancy has not gone entirely unnoticed and hence, at an international conference on ETS at McGill University in Montreal, Canada, in 1989, it was very cautiously suggested that, instead of blaming smokers:

'The possibility that the acute responses noted in some asthmatics result from a psychogenic [in the mind] reaction, as opposed to a physiologic [physical] response to ETS, needs to be investigated further. Psychological and emotional influences are known to be of considerable importance in asthmatic episodes. It has been reported that suggestion may even affect pulmonary [lung] function in non-asthmatics' (Philip Witorsch writing in Environmental Tobacco Smoke, Lexington Books, 1989).

• The above information is an extract of a factsheet from FOREST's web site which can be found at www.forest-on-smoking.org.uk
© FOREST

Half an hour of passive smoking can harm heart

By David Derbyshire

Inhaling second-hand tobacco smoke for just 30 minutes is enough to cause temporary damage to the heart, a study has shown.

Anti-smoking campaigners said the findings offered compelling proof that passive smoking was a health risk and called for a ban on smoking in the workplace.

Previous studies have shown that exposure to second-hand smoke at home increases the risks of heart disease by a third.

The new research, in the *Journal of the American Medical Association*, is the first to look at the effects of second-hand smoke directly on coronary circulation.

Researchers from Osaka City University in Japan measured the effects on the cells that line the cavities of the heart and blood vessels – the 'endothelial' cells.

Normal healthy endothelial cells promote the widening of blood vessels and help to prevent the build-up of fatty deposits on the walls of blood vessels, or atherosclorosis, and formation of clots.

But if the cells malfunction, there is a risk of narrowing blood vessels, atherosclorosis and blood clots.

A non-invasive ultra-sound technique assessed how well the endothelial cells were doing using a measure called 'coronary flow velocity reserve'.

It was measured in 15 smokers and 15 non-smokers before and after a 30-minute exposure to tobacco smoke. They found no change in smokers' blood vessels but those of non-smokers were altered by exposure to passive smoking.

'This provides direct evidence of a harmful effect of passive smoking on the coronary circulation in non-smokers,' the scientists, led by Dr Ryo Otsuka, said.

Clive Bates, director of Action on Smoking and Health, said: 'It is as if the blood vessels in the heart react suddenly to small doses of tobacco smoke, almost like an allergic reaction or spasm.

'Passive smoking has a serious impact on the heart and is a real killer, not just a nuisance or irritation. People claim they have a right to

> **'This provides direct evidence of a harmful effect of passive smoking on the coronary circulation in non-smokers'**

smoke but not if it means non-smokers have to suffer damage to their circulation.

'If something as hazardous as cigarette smoking was leaking from a pipe in a factory, inspectors would close it down. Yet there are still three million non-smokers in Britain who are frequently or continuously exposed to tobacco smoke at work.'

ASH urged the Government to stop blocking the formal code of practice on passive smoking in the workplace promised three years ago.

Prof Sir Charles George, medical director of the British Heart Foundation, said: 'People who do not wish to smoke should have the right to avoid the harmful effects of passive smoking, a hazard that is confirmed by a growing body of evidence.'

20 cigarettes across the EU

The table does not give a comparison for the same brand across the EU. It is based on the Most Popular Price Category (MPPC) in each Member State using information available at 1/10/2001. Values are shown in pence. Totals may not add up due to rounding.

	Retail price	VAT	Ad Valorem	Specific	Total Tax	Tax Incidence
UK	**£4.39**	**£0.65**	**£0.97**	**£1.85**	**£3.46**	**78.9%**
Ireland	£3.01	£0.50	£0.57	£1.28	£2.35	78.1%
Denmark	£2.74	£0.55	£0.58	£1.01	£2.14	78.0%
Finland	£2.47	£0.45	£1.24	£0.19	£1.87	75.6%
Sweden	£2.32	£0.46	£0.91	£0.25	£1.62	70.25
France	£2.07	£0.35	£1.14	£0.08	£1.57	76.0%
Belgium	£1.82	£0.32	£0.84	£0.19	£1.35	73.8%
Netherlands	£1.75	£0.28	£0.36	£0.64	£1.28	73.0%
Germany	£1.83	£0.25	£0.37	£0.61	£1.26	68.9%
Austria	£1.66	£0.28	£0.70	£0.24	£1.21	72.9%
Greece	£1.45	£0.22	£0.78	£0.05	£1.05	72.3%
Italy	£1.34	£0.22	£0.73	£0.05	£1.00	74.5%
Luxembourg	£1.38	£0.15	£0.65	£0.13	£0.93	67.0%
Portugal	£1.14	£0.17	£0.30	£0.43	£0.90	78.6%
Spain	£1.15	£0.16	£0.62	£0.04	£0.82	71.0%

Source: The Tobacco Manufacturers' Association (TMA)

There'll soon be no smoke without ire

American who helped banish smoking from California now has Britain in his sights

With its genuine Tudor timber frame, cobbled street outside and real ales on tap, the Three Fishes pub in Shrewsbury doesn't look like it is leading one of the most controversial, divisive revolutions threatening to sweep the country.

But despite its quaint village appearance, it is at the forefront of a movement that its adherents claim is inevitable to protect human rights and save lives – and its critics claim will destroy thousands of jobs and is bordering on the fascist.

Customers are warned they are entering this battle zone by a little sign by the door: 'No Smoking'. Of the 60,000 pubs in the country, the Three Fishes is one of only four that is totally non-smoking.

'A lot of the regulars and the tourists absolutely love it, and some go completely over the top in supporting you,' said the landlady, Avril Wardop, who says it is part of the reason business is up 30 per cent in the last two years. 'They like the fact that they can walk in the pub and the air is fresh, and they can go home at the end of the night and their clothes don't smell of smoke. We like it because we work here and live here.'

But pubs like the Three Fishes could soon be commonplace. The campaign to ban smoking from places of work and recreation was given a huge boost last week by Stanton Glantz, professor of medicine at the University of California.

Dubbed the tobacco companies' public enemy number one, Glantz has successfully persuaded California and other US states to ban smoking in all bars and restaurants, helped to launch a successful $208 billion compensation claim against tobacco companies, and inspired *The Insider*, a Hollywood film of how tobacco companies fought back.

By Anthony Browne
The Observer

Last week Glantz came to Britain to persuade the Department of Health and the Cabinet Office of the merits of banning smoking in all public places, and gave evidence to a Greater London Assembly inquiry on why public smoking should be banned in the capital. His visit coincided with the publication of the most damning evidence so far on the effects of passive smoking: just half an hour of passive smoking can leave the heart of a non-smoker looking as diseased as the heart of a smoker.

> *People and children in the UK have virtually no legal protection from passive smoking. People have no right to a smoke-free work environment. Taxi drivers cannot even declare their own taxi a smoke-free zone*

'I feel like I'm in a time warp here, it's like we're in California in 1985. There are smokers who are

unapologetic and non-smokers are frightened to say much, but surveys show that people are angry. You're having the same arguments and debates we had, but the idea is spreading very, very quickly, and the science is becoming overwhelming,' said Glantz in the bar of his London hotel, surrounded by smokers.

Glantz believes passionately that no one should have to breathe in second-hand smoke. 'Smokers have a right to smoke. It's stupid, but I'm fat and that's stupid. Everyone is allowed to be stupid, but they should not be allowed to do something stupid that hurts other people.'

The evidence of the dangers of passive smoking is becoming convincing. According to the anti-smoking lobby group Ash, second-hand smoke in the UK is responsible for 623 cancers and 13,000 cases of heart disease each year. It leads to 300,000 middle-ear infections and exacerbates asthma in about 200,000 people. Young children are most susceptible: passive smoking causes 3,800 low birthweight babies each year, kills 200 babies from cot deaths, and 44 from bronchitis.

Yet people and children in the UK have virtually no legal protection from passive smoking. People have no right to a smoke-free work environment. Taxi drivers cannot even declare their own taxi a smoke-free zone: it is actually illegal for them to insist that passengers don't smoke. Child minders working at home are allowed to smoke over the children they are looking after with the consent of the parents: the children have no right to protection. Even hospitals are not required to be smoke-free.

'Half the workers in Britain are getting exposed to high doses of toxic chemicals at work. There is no reason that in a place of work people should have to breathe in benzene and formaldehyde and the other emissions from a little toxic waste dump that is on fire. They deserve to be protected,' said Glantz.

Jo Gaffikin of Forest, the Freedom Organisation for the Right to Enjoy Smoking Tobacco, a lobby group paid for by the tobacco industry, said: 'It's an issue of choice. It's very extreme to me, terribly strident, there's no accommodation made for smokers. People should be allowed to smoke if they want to.'

According to SmokeFree London, an alliance of health authorities campaigning for a ban on smoking in workplaces, bars and restaurants, the public are demanding protection. It commissioned a survey which showed that the majority of smokers and non-smokers thought there ought to be an outright ban on smoking in fast-food outlets and enclosed shopping centres. A majority of non-smokers, but only 25 per cent of smokers, thought there ought to be an outright ban in restaurants.

Judith Watts, co-ordinator of SmokeFree London, said: 'Public opinion is way ahead of political opinion. The public are crying out for protection from second-hand smoke, and meanwhile the Government is dithering.'

The key, according to Glantz, is to change people's attitudes so that smoking is unacceptable. In 1988 California started an incredibly aggressive anti-smoking campaign and within seven years the tobacco industry had lost sales of cigarettes worth $4bn.

In Britain, it is considered rude to ask someone to stop smoking. Parties in the Golden State are now generally non-smoking – no one will ask whether it is all right to smoke, they will just go outside. Smokers are considered very rude if they don't ask permission before they light up.

Smoking is now banned in public places in many cities and states across the US, and across the world. The High Court in The Netherlands recently ruled that all employees are entitled to be protected from smoke at work. A growing number of provinces in Australia, including New South Wales and Victoria, have banned smoking in restaurants.

People in the UK are being

increasingly protected from passive smoke, but it is solely due to voluntary action by companies. Flights are routinely non-smoking, and an increasing number of train companies, such as Virgin, now ban it in all carriages. Cinemas are now almost all non-smoking, and about half the pubs in Britain have areas set aside for non-smokers, and a growing number of restaurants are smoke-free. Some chains like Wetherspoons automatically have non-smoking areas, and don't allow smoking by the bar.

A majority of non-smokers, but only 25 per cent of smokers, thought there ought to be an outright ban in restaurants

---

Bars and restaurants are very keen to avoid legislation. They have set up a 'charter group', entirely

funded by the tobacco industry, to encourage outlets to set their own policies.

Nick Bish, the chairman of the hospitality industry's committee on smoking in public places, said: 'We want to keep the Government off our backs. We believe that by having separate areas and good ventilation, and telling customers, they can make an informed decision.'

Ian McKerracher, chief executive of the Restaurant Association, said: 'Restaurants should have the right to decide the policies they want. If customers don't like the policies of a restaurant, eat somewhere else. If the staff don't like the policies of an employer, don't work there – work somewhere else.'

But according to Clive Bates, director of Ash, non-smokers are becoming hardline: 'If you look at how people react on trains and in cinemas to people who smoke, you see how attitudes are changing. People are given permission to object by the small non-smoking signs. It's not a small annoyance, it's a major annoyance that is suppressed. There is an underlying substrate of concern and anger that will take us to a ban.'

Glantz predicted it won't be long before the UK follows the US and Australia. 'You'll be surprised about how suddenly things change. You push and push and once it starts moving, it slides.'

• This article first appeared in *The Observer*, 29 July, 2001.

Smoking in public places

Information from FOREST

The frequency with which anti-smokers talk about banning smoking in 'public places' would lead one to believe that there is a clearly defined concept of what constitutes a 'public place'. In practice it is not that easy, a fact acknowledged by a speaker at the 1998 annual conference of the British Medical Association (BMA) who asked, 'If a person was having a cigarette on the summit of Snowdonia, should they be stopped?'

(*Western Mail*, 9th July 1998).

This isn't quite as absurd as you might think. Writing in the *Financial Times* (10th October 1998), journalist Simon Tiffin reported that:

'After a hard day's skiing the trails of Vail in Colorado, I was standing on top of a Rocky Mountain peak admiring the landscape and savouring that Big Country flavour of a thousand Marlboro advertisements. Suddenly my musings were abruptly interrupted: "Excuse me, but would you mind putting that out?" said an offended voice with a Californian twang. In the Land of the Free, a smoker is not safe even on a mountain top.'

Kenneth Clarke (now a director of British American Tobacco) suffered a similar experience. Interviewed in FOREST's *Free Choice* magazine (Spring 2000), he recalled an incident in Canada's Rocky Mountains:

'There were probably more bears than people when a middle-aged American woman, who I could see in the distance some three or four hundred yards away, scrambled over rocks, through brambles, and said would I warn her if I was going to smoke again because it gave her migraine. She must have been using binoculars to see that I was smoking so I think her migraine had more to do with her state of mind than it had to do with my cigar.'

Definition of a 'public place'

The phrase 'public place' usually means an enclosed interior and there is therefore a question of ownership. Most people distinguish between two types of property. The first are buildings funded by the public (for example, council offices); the second are those that are privately owned (pubs, restaurants, hotels, even taxi cabs). However, because each type of property is visited by the public, anti-smokers believe they can dictate what the policy on smoking should be.

The list of what is included in the term 'public places' grows ever longer and now includes all manner of privately-owned premises, including entire shopping malls (where people are encouraged to stay for several hours) and, most notably, pubs and restaurants

The problem is that if society accepts the view that privately-

owned pubs and restaurants are 'public places' the definition won't stop there. Some, like Dr Vetter of the South Glamorgan Division of the British Medical Association, already want to go even further and define a 'public place' as a place where any member of the public might conceivably find himself. Addressing the BMA's 1999 Annual Conference, Dr Vetter actually proposed that smokers should only be able to light up in the privacy of their own bathroom, the rest of the house being considered to be a 'public place'.

Ban on smoking is bad for business

Businesses, especially in the hospitality trade, would have good reason to resist legislation forcing them to ban smokers. Their instinct, experience and survey after survey tell them that their business is sure to suffer if they introduce a total ban on smoking. The senior vice-chairman of Nottingham and Notts Licensed Victuallers recognised this when he told the *Nottingham Evening Post* (26th December 1995), *'The pub environment is where most smokers congregate. Pubs seem synonymous with smoking.'*

That is why so few establishments ban smoking altogether. We continually hear about venues introducing no-smoking zones or other restrictions (and who can blame them for accepting the free press coverage that accompanies such announcements?) but we rarely hear about it when the policy is quietly dropped some months later.

A report from the Restaurant Association reveals that £346 million could be lost in income and 45,000 jobs if restaurants were forced to ban smokers. No surprise then that a number of prominent restaurateurs have strong views on the matter.

They include FOREST patron Antony Worrall Thompson who told one dogmatic anti-smoker on television: '*If you're so vociferous about non-smoking, and the majority of non-smokers aren't, there is enough choice to find good food where there are perfectly good non-smoking areas. You don't have to come to my restaurant.*'

Michael Gottlieb (owner, London's Cafe Spice) said: '*72 per cent may not smoke, but they don't all object to other smokers. The consumer has a choice. If ultimately they don't want to go to a restaurant that has too much smoke, they will go elsewhere, and that restaurateur is going to suffer. It's really as straightforward as that*' (*Food & Drink*, BBC2, 7th December 1998)

Terence Conran (designer/restaurant owner) said: '*My personal attitude to smoking is that adults should be allowed to do what they wish as long as it does not upset reasonable people or break the law*' (*London Evening Standard*, 25th September 1998).

Pru Leith (Leith's restaurant) said: '*A voluntary approach rather than a legislative ban must be the way forward*' (letter published in *The Times*, 17th September 1998).

Michel Roux (chef de cuisine at Le Gavroche in London) said: '*While I gave up [smoking] eight years ago I would certainly not presume to impose my views on anybody else to give up such a pleasure*' (*Sunday Business*, 19th July 1998).

Regular surveys of the hospitality trade, especially pubs, have confirmed what non-prejudiced eyes will tell you – that while non-smokers outnumber smokers 2:1 in society at large, in many pubs the ratio is often reversed, and in some pubs smokers represent an overwhelming majority.

Evidence of the negative effect of a ban on smoking

History is littered with examples of establishments that have introduced smoking bans only to experience a drop in custom, sometimes quite dramatically, with the result that they eventually have to reverse the policy months (or years) later.

In 1991 the management committee of Devizes Leisure Centre asked Kennet District Council for permission to lift the smoking ban because the bar was constantly empty and no one wanted to hire it for functions. Although some councillors argued that to allow smoking was contrary to their role in health promotion, they nevertheless voted to permit a designated smoking area to boost business. Likewise Peterborough City Council was forced to reverse its no-smoking policy in social centres after discovering that in the seven months since a ban was brought in, it had cost them £7,500 in lettings (*The Times*, 24th July 1995).

One of the first examples of the consequences of banning smoking in a pub took place in 1993. Acting on assurances that customers wanted it, Donna Swinburn, landlady of the Smugglers in Roker, Sunderland, introduced a blanket ban. The outcome was radically different from what she had been led to believe. After five months the pub had lost £14,000 in takings. Within a week of reversing the ban income rose again by 25%.

We continually hear about venues introducing no-smoking zones or other restrictions but we rarely hear about it when the policy is quietly dropped some months later

---

In April 1998 Freud's Bar on Shaftesbury Avenue, London, announced that it would be operating a no-smoking policy four nights a week for a trial period of one month. To begin with management were quite bullish about their bold initiative. Predictably, however, the outcome of this anti-smoking experiment was a loss of custom. A spokesman admitted that the number of customers had gone down because the bar immediately lost its die-hard smokers and failed to attract sufficient new customers to make up the loss. Rather wistfully he told the *East Anglian Daily Times*, '*It probably needs one of the bigger chains to do it for a whole year for it to really take off*' (22nd May 1998).

This also proved to be incorrect, as exemplified by Toby Restaurants' attempt to ban smoking in 1996. Within months the company announced that, '*Individual managers have experienced some strongly-held local views and will try to meet specific smoking requirements*' (*The Publican*, 18th March 1996).

In May 1998 the Royal Oak, at East Bergholt near Ipswich, announced that it was introducing a no-smoking room and duly received coverage in the local press. No such fanfares, however, when it was later announced that the 'no-smoking room' would henceforth be open to smokers. According to the owners, '*When we opened it there was a positive response from a lot of people, who said they would use it. But I'm afraid for quite a number of them it's been a case of saying one thing and doing another*' (*Licensee & Morning Advertiser*, 28th September 1998).

Also in 1998, a Newcastle restaurateur abandoned his no-smoking policy as a costly failure. Trentino Carpinelli admitted, '*We opened with a no-smoking policy but it did not work. It has cost me quite a lot of money*' (*Newcastle Journal*, 24th October 1998). He also said that non-smokers were not making bookings because they did not want to leave out friends in their party who smoked.

In January 2000 publican John Sims announced that he was selling his no-smoking pub, the Three Fishes in Shrewsbury. After introducing his ban in 1994, Sims revelled in the publicity, appearing on television and radio. In 1996 he was even nominated for an Entrepreneur of the Year award. Four years later Sims told his local paper, the *Shropshire Star* (10th January 2000), that it had been a struggle to make the idea of a smoke-free pub work and that he felt a little let down because the venture had 'not had the support from non-smokers' and 'I do feel as if I have suffered for standing up for non-smokers.'

• The above information is an extract from FOREST's web site which can be found at www.forest-on-smoking.org.uk

Smoking in the workplace

Information from UNISON

This article is intended for members who have concerns over smoking in the workplace.

There are a number of issues of relevance to UNISON members:

- the health risks,
- the legal position,
- the rights of smokers, and
- the drafting of workplace policies.

The issue for the workplace is not whether employees smoke but where they smoke, and not whether a non-smoking policy should be introduced but how it is introduced.

Health risks

Smoking is the main cause of preventable disease and premature death. It is now recognised that smoking not only affects smokers, but also non-smokers through passive smoking. This is when non-smokers breathe in the smoke from other people's cigarettes. In addition to putting smokers and non-smokers at risk from diseases such as lung cancer, it can also act as an irritant on the eyes, throat, respiratory tract; aggravate asthma; and pose a threat to the unborn child. The HSE has identified tobacco smoke and in-adequate ventilation as factors contributing to sick building syndrome. This list is not exhaustive.

The legal position

Under Section 2 of the Health and Safety at Work Act 1974 employers must protect the health of employees and provide a healthy and safe working environment. Under the Control of Substances Hazardous to Health Regulations 1994 employers must ensure that wherever possible employees are not exposed to hazardous substances. With today's level of awareness on passive smoking it would be difficult for any employer to argue that they are not in breach of these duties by not prohibiting smoking at work in all areas except for specifically designated places where non-smokers have no reason to enter.

UNISON
the public service union

Regulation 25(3) of the Workplace Health, Safety and Welfare Regulations 1992 requires that rest rooms and rest areas have suitable arrangements to protect non-smokers from the discomfort of tobacco smoke, such as separate rest facilities or the prohibition of smoking at these places. The HSE have published an Approved Code of Practice on Smoking which is likely to come into force in early 2001.

Case law also requires employers to provide a safe workplace, so that they may be sued for negligence where exposure to passive smoke damages the health of employees. Two UNISON members with permanent damage to their health due to smoky offices with inadequate ventilation received compensation from their employer.

In 1993 Veronica Bland received £15,000 from Stockport Metropolitan Borough Council. She

suffered years of passive smoking at work and eventually developed chronic bronchitis. In 1995 Beryl Roe received £25,000 compensation from Stockport Council. She had to retire on ill-health grounds after suffering eye, nose, throat, and bronchial hypersensitivity which returns if she goes into a smoky atmosphere. The council had increased her exposure by shutting down the ventilation system in her office.

It is therefore not only in the interests of non-smokers, but also in the interests of employers to provide an adequate no-smoking policy. However this does not mean simply imposing a blanket ban without any consultation, which is least likely to work. Any policy must take into account the need of all employees. The HSE states that in some situations a complete ban may be justified for safety reasons, but the imposition of such elsewhere without proper consultation can lead to resentment and enforcement problems.

In Dryden v Greater Glasgow Health Board 1992, after extensive consultations with and 3 months' notice to all employees the employer

revised its no-smoking policy to ban smoking anywhere on its premises. Previously smoking had been permitted in a 'smoking' coffee room and in a part of the canteen. Counselling and support was offered to those wishing to give up. Ms Dryden found that time constraints meant that it was difficult for her to leave the premises in order to smoke. She therefore resigned and claimed constructive dismissal. It was decided that the right to smoke was a personal habit and not an implied contractual term and therefore she did not have the right to smoke at work. It is however important to note that one factor in reaching this decision was that the issue of a smoking ban had been handled as sympathetically as possible and with full consultation.

What UNISON wants from employers

- Sensible no-smoking policies – an employer recently attempted to increase the working week for employees who took smoking breaks by requiring them to work an extra half-hour each day. Directly attacking employees' conditions of services is not a helpful approach and is one which UNISON will continue to oppose;
- Consultation with safety representatives and branches over the introduction and content of such policies – since this is a health and safety issue there is a right to consultation. The HSE recognises that full in-depth consultation with employees and their representatives is highly desirable for the smooth implementation of smoking policies;
- Smoke-free work areas with good ventilation;
- Non-smoking rest rooms;
- Where appropriate, decent and well-ventilated smoking rooms – with a separate ventilation system so that smoke is not re-circulated into the rest of the building;
- Stress-free work so that smokers are not driven to smoke; and
- Help for smokers who wish to cut down or give up – this could include paid time off and the cost of attending sessions which help smokers to give up, and payments for nicotine patches.

A smoke-free work environment will: support those trying to give up, provide cleaner air for everybody, and help employers to avoid liability.

What makes a good no-smoking policy?

A no-smoking policy has to be carefully drawn up and introduced in order to ensure that it works.

1. *Negotiation in consultation with the union*:
Policies which are imposed without consultation and with no provision for smokers are less likely to succeed.

2. *Tailoring the policy to the needs of the particular workplace*:
UNISON members work in a wide variety of workplaces, with varying degrees of contact with patients, clients and the public. Some work shifts or nights. There is no blueprint for a successful policy. Account must be taken of local circumstances and the particular characteristics of the work and workplace.

3. *A clear, strong commitment to health promotion*:
The policy should be about improving health in general rather than just bringing in action to limit smoking. The policy should seek to protect or promote the health of both the smoker and the non-smoker.
Full support and encouragement should be offered to smokers who want to stop smoking and those that feel they are unable to. Help to smokers should include a health education programme, with time off and fees paid if necessary to attend courses on giving up smoking. Payment for nicotine patches and gum could also be provided.
Branches should also raise the wider issues which may be encouraging

workplace smoking such as stress and high workloads. The HSE recognises that stress at work can lead people to smoke more.

4. *Make provisions for smokers*:
Separate smoking areas rather than a complete ban which could alienate smokers and lead to activities such as smoking in toilets. It must be recognised that smoking is an addiction and most smokers would find it very difficult to give up smoking at work.

5. *Providing information*:
Information about the issues should be provided to members whilst the policy is being drawn up and implemented.

6. *Setting up a working party*:
A management/union working party should involve smokers, non-smokers and ex-smokers.

7. *Timescale for implementation*:
It is important that a policy is not drawn up in a rush and imposed by management without full consultation. Time will need to be taken to get the policy right and ensure the majority of members are happy with it. There should be at least a 12-week time gap between the policy being finalised and it coming into force.

8. *Covering everyone*:
A policy should cover everyone – staff and management, visitors, clients and patients.

9. *Making everyone aware of the policy*:
There must be procedures for making everyone aware of the policy, including clients, visitors and patients.

10. *Monitoring the policy*:
The policy must be monitored and reviewed to ensure it is working effectively, to make changes if necessary and to ensure that any problems or complaints are picked up and dealt with fairly.

- The above information is an extract from a factsheet produced by UNISON and is available from their web site which can be found at www.unison.org.uk

© UNISON

Smoking in the workplace

Smoking in the workplace needs to be addressed, banning it outright may not be the best answer and a poorly conceived smoking policy will have a negative effect

1. Employers need to address the issue of smoking in the workplace

- 30% of adults in Britain smoke, therefore it can be assumed that up to 30% of your workforce are smokers.
- It is inevitable that legislation affecting smoking in the workplace will be forthcoming, either from the UK Government or Europe, and that when it is in place it will be complex and rapidly changing.
- A number of regulations relevant to smoking policies are already in place, which employers need to be aware of.
- All employees have a right to work in an environment free from harmful chemicals found in most workplaces.
- A lack of action is not a viable alternative, since it places an employer in a position of contravening current regulations and open to civil actions brought by current or former employee; both smokers and non-smokers.
- Employees should not be discriminated against, simply because they smoke.

2. Prohibition is not necessarily the best answer

The emotive nature of the smoking debate can often mean that common sense and consideration are pushed to the bottom of the list when employers and managers consider what type of smoking policy to introduce. The prohibition of smoking in the workplace without consultation is not the best solution and this has been demonstrated by a number of organisations which have reversed total smoking bans following problems of implementation.

Promoting equal rights for smokers

3. The consequences of a poorly conceived policy will have a negative effect

A lack of consultation within the workplace can lead to smokers feeling that they are being discriminated against and, as a result, increase tension among staff – and between management and staff – adversely affecting their morale. (74% of employers don't even ask about the sort of smoking policy that should be introduced.* 1 in 2 non-smokers believe that smokers are being discriminated against within the workplace, rising to 2 in 3 non-smoking trade unionists.**)

A complete smoking ban within the workplace can lead to increased stress on individuals which in turn will result in reduced efficiency.

The failure to make proper provision for smokers within the premises leaves them no alternative but to smoke at, or nearby, the entrance to the premises. This reflects badly on the employer, for it illustrates an inconsiderate attitude towards staff who smoke, and looks unpleasant for any client approaching to do business. People will inevitably try to smoke within the premises, generally in places where it is inadvisable. A fire risk could therefore be created where none had previously existed.

There is no excuse for a poorly devised smoking policy

Smoking in the workplace should be approached like any other workplace issue – as a management problem – rather than allowing emotion to govern the decision-making process.

Information and advice on matters such as current regulations, legislation, technology to assist, the pitfalls, examples of good practice, are readily available to both the individual and employer.

A solution that accommodates both non-smokers and smokers has to be better than one which discriminates.

The correct time to create provision for smoking within the fabric of a building is during the design stages of a refurbishment or a new build.

* City of London Survey dated 29 September 1997
** FOREST TUC Conference Survey 1997

• The above information is an extract from FOREST's web site which can be found at www.forest-on-smoking.org.uk

© FOREST

Pub lobby blocks ban on smoking at work

The Government has scrapped planned tough new curbs on smoking in the workplace after fierce lobbying from the pub and restaurant trade.

It quietly rejected advice from the independent Health and Safety Commission for a legal code forcing all employers either to ban smoking or take stringent other measures to protect staff from second-hand smoke.

Ministers told the watchdog to redraft proposals giving more ground to the hospitality industry – which complained that it would either have to stop customers lighting up or take expensive steps to protect bar staff and waiters – and examining the use of voluntary agreements.

The move delays any chance of a passive-smoking crackdown, angering the anti-tobacco lobby and irritating senior figures at the HSC. Although a code will still be produced, campaigners fear it will be so watered down as to be barely worth it.

'If the Government have given in to the pressure then I am extremely disappointed,' said Labour peeress Baroness Gibson, who sat on the committee that drafted the original code.

'It certainly undermines their strategy. If you are trying to get an anti-smoking policy in offices and places like that, if the minute you leave the office and go to the pub or out for a meal there isn't a smoking ban, your health is being endangered.'

She said there had been 'heavy lobbying' from the leisure industry and the HSC had already made compromises in its first draft. 'I think that the leisure industry is being extremely selfish, it is endangering people's health,' she said.

Unveiled last September, the code would have forced employers

to take action either by banning smoking; or segregating smokers by, for example, creating special rooms for them; or if this was impracticable, by installing better ventilation, or changing shifts to reduce the time staff were exposed to smoking customers. Firms that took insufficient action would have faced prosecution and heavy fines.

The hospitality industry complained that it would either have to stop customers lighting up or take expensive steps to protect bar staff and waiters

---

Studies have repeatedly shown links between inhaling second-hand smoke and heart disease, lung cancer, and stroke as well as cot death in babies. Hundreds of people die prematurely every year from passive smoking-related illness.

The HSC was originally asked to produce a code in 1998, under the then Health Secretary Frank Dobson's anti-smoking strategy which promised a significant 'toughening of measures' against passive smoking.

The HSC will now consider other options including creating separate rules for pubs and restaurants. Anti-smoking campaigners say that is not enough.

'The original code was perfectly sensible, perfectly sound, and there is no reason at all for them to do this,' said Clive Bates, of the pressure group Action on Smoking and Health.

An HSC spokeswoman said the new proposals needed to 'strike the right balance' between small business and staff welfare.

The news comes within days of the Government granting a fresh concession to the tobacco industry. Cigarette manufacturers are expected to be given an extra two years to comply with a European Union-wide agreement reducing tar levels in products made for export.

• This article first appeared in *The Observer*, 29 July, 2001. By Gaby Hinsliff, Chief Political Correspondent.

© *Guardian Newspapers Limited 2001*

Stopping smoking

ASH's 15 Tips

ash.
action on smoking and health

1. Get professional help . . .

Ring the helpline on Freephone 0800 169 0 169 for information and advice. Pregnant women seeking help in stopping smoking can call the pregnancy Quitline on 0800 169 9169. Specialist helplines are also available in Asian languages. Your doctor, pharmacist, or health visitor should also give advice and they should tell you if there are special services for smokers in your area. ASH's quit smoking resources give a good overview of other sites and materials on the ASH site and internet.

2. Prepare mentally . . .

You are not alone! 70% of British smokers would like to quit and about three million try each year. More than 11 million people in Britain have quit and are now ex-smokers. However, it can be tough and you will need lots of willpower to break the hold of nicotine – a powerful and addictive drug. An important part of this is to know what you would gain and what you would lose from stopping smoking. One ex-60-a-day smoker (Allen Carr, author of best-selling *The Easy Way to Stop Smoking*) says: 'there is absolutely nothing to give up . . . there is no genuine pleasure or crutch in smoking. It is just an illusion, like banging your head against a wall to make it pleasant when you stop.'

3. Demolish smoking myths . . .

Soon after smoking a cigarette the body and brain start to want more nicotine and many people begin to feel increasingly uncomfortable until they have the next cigarette. Smoking feels pleasurable, but much of the pleasure of smoking is relief of withdrawal from nicotine. There are times that many people feel distracted or unable to enjoy themselves because they were not able to smoke. This is nicotine withdrawal in action. If you see it this way, cigarettes are not a familiar friend but more like a greedy parasite demanding constant attention.

4. Understand what to expect . . .

Most people find the first few days difficult and for some it can be a long struggle, but things will typically start to get better after the third or fourth day. Nicotine withdrawal may make you restless, irritable, frustrated, sleepless, or accident prone – but

There is absolutely nothing to give up . . . there is no genuine pleasure or crutch in smoking. It is just an illusion

these things will pass and you will quickly start to feel the benefits. See the ASH fact sheet on what happens when you give up smoking.

5. Make a list of reasons why you want to stop smoking . . .

It means different things to different people, but if you know what you want from stopping, it could help you through the most difficult moments. Reasons could include some or all of:

- Better all-round health – stopping smoking reduces risk of 50 different illnesses and conditions
- Heart attack risk drops to the same as a non-smoker three years after quitting
- Cancer risk drops with every year of not smoking
- Live longer and stay well – one in two long-term smokers die early and lose about 16 years of life
- Set a good example to the kids (or other people's kids) – don't want to be a smoking role model
- Have lots of money to spend on other things – smoking 20 a day can cost £1,400 per year

The cost of smoking

Consider the money. Main brand cigarettes currently cost £4.33 after the March 2001 budget. The table shows how much smoking costs at current prices.

Cigarettes per day	Years of smoking				
	1	5	10	20	50
5	£3.95	£1,976	£3,951	£7,902	£19,756
10	£790	£3,951	£7,902	£15,805	£39,511
20	£1,580	£7,902	£15,805	£31,609	£79,023
40	£3,161	£15,805	£31,609	£63,218	£158,045

Source: ASH - Action on Smoking and Health

- Improved fitness and easier breathing – better at sports and getting up stairs
- Better chance of having a healthy baby
- Food and drink tastes better
- Better skin and complexion, and no early wrinkles
- Fresher smelling breath, hair and clothes, and no more cigarette smells around the house
- Back in full control and no longer craving or distracted when I am not smoking or not able to smoke
- Travel on trains, aircraft, buses will be easier
- Work will be easier and I won't have to spend so much time outside or in the smoking room
- Don't want to support tobacco companies
- Concern about environmental impact of tobacco growing
- Other . . .

6. Consider the money . . .

Main brand cigarettes currently cost £4.33 after the March 2001 budget. The table shows how much smoking costs at current prices.

7. Set a date . . .

Some people make a New Year's Day resolution, others pick their birthday, and you can join in with others on No Smoking Day – the second Wednesday of every March – when up to a million smokers have a go. Any day will do, but choosing a date will help mental preparation.

8. Involve friends or family . . .

If you live with someone else that smokes, it will be much easier to quit if you do it together. When expecting a baby, both parents should do it together. One common mistake is not to take the effort to quit smoking seriously enough. Really putting your whole commitment behind it will help you have the right frame of mind to face the challenge.

9. Deal with nicotine withdrawal . . .

Nicotine is a powerful addictive drug (see ASH fact sheet on nicotine) and you can roughly double the chances of successfully quitting smoking by using nicotine replacement therapies such as patches,

lozenges, inhalers, and/or gum. The idea is to come off nicotine gradually by using a low nicotine dose to take the edge off the cravings and have a 'soft landing'. Nicotine products include Nicorette , NiQuitin CQ and Nicotinell. An alternative to nicotine products is the drug Zyban which is only available on prescription. Although it is proven to be effective, as with all drugs there is a risk of side effects and you will need to discuss with your doctor whether this form of therapy would be suitable for you.

10. Other treatments may help . . .

Hypnosis, acupuncture or other treatments may help some people, but there isn't much formal evidence supporting their effectiveness. Our advice is to use with caution, but even if they help mental preparation, then they have some value. Herbal cigarettes are pointless – you get all the tar, but nothing to help you deal with nicotine withdrawal. Quit has a good guide to treatments.

11. Find a (temporary) substitute habit . . .

Smoking also involves having something to do with the hands or mouth. Non-smokers manage without this, so it will not be necessary in the long term. But if this is part of the smoking habit, you may need to deal with it. It might be an idea to use chewing gum, drink

---

Stop completely . . . Although it might seem like a good idea to cut down and then stop, this is actually very difficult to do in practice

---

more water, fruit juice or tea, or to chew or eat something (but see weight gain below!).

12. Deal with any weight-gain worries . . .

Yes it is true: many people do gain weight when they quit smoking. Nicotine changes the appetite and body's energy use (metabolism). Even if you do gain weight it will be worth it if you quit, but if you want to avoid weight-gain then you can prepare. For example, you can change your diet or avoid alcohol, or take more exercise. (You may find QUIT's guide *Quitting smoking without putting on weight* helpful.)

13. Avoid temptation . . .

In the difficult first few days you can change your routine to avoid situations where you would usually smoke. For example, it might be worth avoiding the pub on the first Friday night after you quit.

14. Stop completely . . .

Although it might seem like a good idea to cut down and then stop, this is actually very difficult to do in practice. If you cut down, the likely response is that you will smoke each cigarette more intensively and end up doing yourself just as much harm. The best approach is to go for a complete break and use nicotine replacement products (see above) to help take the edge off the withdrawal symptoms.

15. Watch out for relapse . . .

You will need to be on your guard especially in the first few days and weeks. 'I'll have just one, it can't harm' is the top of a long and slippery slope. If you are upset or under pressure, it is really important to fight off the temptation to smoke – don't let this be an excuse for slipping back. You could lose everything you've achieved just in a momentary lapse.

- The above information is an extract from a factsheet produced by ASH. This and other factsheets are available on their web site which can be found at www.ash.org.uk Alternatively see page 41 for their address details.

The QUIT guide to stopping smoking

Most smokers want to stop smoking and it's the single most important thing a smoker can do to live longer. At any one time, about 1 in 6 smokers are trying to quit. It's not easy but more than 12 million people in Britain are now successful ex-smokers. Most of those who stop, do so by themselves. Being determined is the vital ingredient. There is no quick and easy way and nothing can MAKE you stop – but, if you really want to, you can and there are ways you can significantly increase your chances of becoming smoke-free.

Methods and products

There are many different methods and products on the market – so many, that it may seem that people are simply after your money, or you may feel so desperate that you will try anything. It is important to check whether the product is safe and effective before you spend your time, energy and money. The aim of this article is to provide you with a guide to the known facts about the different ways to help you stop smoking. However, if you are in any doubt as to whether it is safe for you to use a product or method, check first with your doctor or pharmacist.

What to believe

Some manufacturers claim very high success rates for their products, promising 80-90% effortless success. Yet there is no magic solution. To be certain that a product or method works it has to be put through proper tests (clinical trials). If the product has an effect, it can then be compared to that achieved with another product. Not all the products available have been tested in this way.

A smoking cessation aid CANNOT
- Do the quitting for you
- Make you WANT to stop
- Make it painless and easy.

QUIT®

Helping smokers to quit

A smoking cessation aid CAN
- Ease nicotine withdrawal
- Boost your confidence and morale
- Lessen the urge to smoke.

If you decide to use a smoking cessation product then it's important to know that there are two main types of products – those that contain nicotine and those that do not. This article gives the most up-to-date results of clinical trials.

For help ring QUITLINE® – 0800 00 22 00

Whatever method you choose to quit smoking it is important to have thought it through in advance and prepared yourself as best you can for the difficulties ahead. If you want help with preparation, have a query about a particular product or any aspect of stopping, or want support and encouragement, especially during the difficult times, then Quitline is there to help. Quitline is free and staffed by trained smoking cessation counsellors who will do their best to help you.

Recent independent research published in the research journal Tobacco Control states that Quitline appeared to be 'very successful in helping callers to stop smoking'.

Stop smoking clinics and support groups

Specialist smokers' clinics, often using nicotine replacement products or Zyban, can improve your chances of stopping by up to four times.

Groups can help you to feel less alone in your attempt to quit. Being with other people who are also stopping can provide all-important mutual support, a sense of being understood and a sense of friendly competition!

They are usually run over a period of about six weeks and take you through the different stages of stopping. There are a growing number of NHS specialist clinics and support groups ring Quitline 0800 002200.

Nicotine replacement therapy (NRT)

These products replace some of the nicotine that you used to get from smoking. Nicotine replacement is used to wean you off nicotine by replacing the very high concentrations of nicotine you get from smoking with much lower doses delivered more slowly. It is a means of delivering nicotine without the harmful tar, gases and other elements of smoking. NRT reduces the cravings for cigarettes and the withdrawal symptoms associated with quitting. NRT is the most throughly researched method and tests have shown that, used correctly, it will double your chance of success – which is good news for those who have found withdrawal very hard on previous attempts. If you smoke your first cigarette within 30 minutes of waking, then you are more likely to benefit from NRT.

To check you are using NRT properly, always follow the manufacturers' instructions. Ask your pharmacist or doctor if you are not sure. NRT is much safer than smoking but if you have a medical condition, any health worries or are pregnant, it is important that you talk to your pharmacist /doctor first.

There are several forms of nicotine replacement available – patches, gum, lozenge, nasal spray, inhalator and sublingual (under the tongue) tablets. All of these products are available on NHS prescription. In addition, it is possible to purchase them from pharmacists and some are available from supermarkets and other retail outlets. Many of these products offer programmes of support to help smokers through the quitting process.

The patch gives you a continual supply of nicotine at a low dose while you are wearing it – so you can't respond quickly to a craving or a stressful moment. The gum and the spray deliver a higher dose quickly so you can respond to a craving with a 'quick fix', as with cigarettes. If you smoke steadily through the day, the patch may suit you better. If you smoke mainly in response to cravings or stress, the gum or spray might be more flexible for you. One study has compared the effectiveness of gum, patch, spray and inhalator and found that they are similarly effective.

Patches (Nicotinell, Nicorette, Boots, NiQuitin CQ)

A nicotine skin patch looks like a sticking plaster and is applied to dry non-hairy skin, for example, on the upper arm. A patch lasts either 16 or 24 hours and they come in three strengths, delivering different amounts of nicotine which is absorbed slowly through the skin. You are recommended to use them for 8-12 weeks. For most smokers it is appropriate to start with the highest strength patch. These are easy to use and your nicotine levels build up slowly during the day to help keep the cravings and other withdrawal symptoms away. Although you may still get urges to smoke and thoughts about smoking these are not as strong as before. The main side-effects are itching or redness of the skin and

this can be lessened by varying the position of the patch when you put a new one on. Some people may have problems with sleeping.

The usefulness of patches has been well researched and they can double your chance of quitting. They are most helpful to people who smoke moderately (10-20) and regularly through the day. If you think you are very dependent on nicotine, then another form of nicotine replacement may suit you better. If in doubt seek advice.

Gum (Nicotinell, Nicorette, Boots)

This is different from ordinary chewing gum and can have a peppery or tingling sensation, especially to begin with, so you may have to persevere in using it. It is important to learn to chew it properly to get the full benefit from using it. You should use approximately 1 piece per hour (say 15 pieces per day). It should be chewed slowly and then rested between your gum and the side of your mouth, repeatedly, for about 30 minutes. The nicotine is slowly absorbed through the lining of the mouth. The gum comes in two strengths, low (2mg) and full (4mg) and in a choice of flavours. If the urges to smoke are not relieved sufficiently with the low dose gum, you may need to use the full strength. The recommended period of use is three months. The main side-effect is irritation of the mouth and throat, but this lessens with use. The gum is difficult to use if you wear dentures and can irritate your stomach if you chew too vigorously.

Clinical trials on the gum also show that it can double your success rate. If you smoke heavily (20 or more) then you may need the full strength.

There are many different methods and products on the market – so many, that it may seem that people are simply after your money, or you may feel so desperate that you will try anything

---

A small number of ex-smokers find it hard to stop using the gum after the 3-month period. However, this is a negligible health risk and the need to use it ususally decreases with time. Remember the gum is far safer than cigarette smoking.

Nasal spray (Nicorette)

The nicotine nasal spray comes in a bottle with a nozzle that delivers a dose of a fine spray of nicotine squirted into each nostril. It can be used up to 32 times a day (64 squirts per day). The nicotine is quickly absorbed through the lining of the nose. It mimics the effects of cigarettes more closely by giving a relatively fast effect. It should be used for 3 months, although again a small number of ex-smokers continue to use it beyond this time period. Clinical trials show that it can double your likelihood of quitting, especially if you smoke 20 or more cigarettes a day. It is particularly suitable for highly dependent smokers for whom the other products may not have such an immediate impact.

The spray frequently irritates your nose and throat, for the first few days. It is very important you persevere with it so your nose can adjust to these sensations. After a few days of regular use you should not be troubled by this irritation. If you persevere this lessens after a few days.

Tablets (Nicorette) and lozenges (Nicotinell)

A number of tablets and lozenges containing nicotine are available. The Nicorette Microtab and Nicotinell Lozenge both deliver similar amounts of nicotine as 2 mg gum. Like the gum, the nicotine is absorbed through the lining of the mouth.

Inhalator (Nicorette, Boots)

The inhalator looks like a cigarette holder, inside which you place a cartridge containing nicotine. When you get a craving, you hold the inhalator in your hand, taking shallow puffs (like a pipe) or deep puffs (like a cigarette). Nicotine is taken into the mouth and the back of the throat but not into the lungs. Clinically proven to double your chances of quitting, the inhalator is helpful when your body craves the nicotine and your hands and mouth miss the cigarette.

Effective non-nicotine treatment

Zyban (bupropion hydrochloride SR)

Zyban is a non-nicotine treatment to help smokers who are motivated to quit. It is available on NHS prescription from a GP. Zyban works in the brain to help break the addiction to nicotine and differs from nicotine replacement therapies in that it does not substitute one source of nicotine with another. Zyban reduces the cravings for cigarettes and the withdrawal symptoms associated with quitting. Clinical trials have demonstrated that Zyban doubles your chances of success.

Zyban comes in tablet form; it is taken as a two-month treatment course and costs the charge for a prescription. Smokers should start taking Zyban whilst they are still smoking and set a date for quitting during the second week of treatment, for example, on day eight of taking the tablets. Tablets are usually taken once a day for the first three days, then twice a day for the remainder of the two-month treatment course.

As with any medicine, some people may experience side-effects whilst taking Zyban. The most common ones are difficulty sleeping, dry mouth and headache. These are usually mild and generally disappear within the first few weeks. Many of these effects can also be due to stopping smoking itself as your body adjusts to being without nicotine.

Zyban should not be taken by people who suffer or have ever suffered from seizures (fits), or eating disorders. Your GP will be able to advise whether Zyban is suitable for you having checked your medical history.

Every patient who is prescribed Zyban is offered motivational support from the Right Time ProgrammeTM, which is a personalised programme designed to encourage and support patients throughout their quit attempt. It provides tips and advice on giving up, access to specially trained

QUIT counsellors through a dedicated telephone helpline, a stop smoking action plan and motivational letters timed to arrive at key stages in the quitting process.

Other non-nicotine products

These are many and varied. They are easily available through mail-order, newsagents, health shops or chemists. Often they do not require a licence under the Medicines Act. There is not enough good scientific evidence to say how effective they are. Be wary of claims of very high success rates.

Capsules

Contain menthyl valerate, quinine, camphor and eucolyptus oil aimed at improving breathing and controlling withdrawal symptoms. The manufacturers recommend 1-2 per day for 28 days. There is no evidence of their long-term efficacy, but they are not thought to be harmful. Because of the herbal contents, pregnant women should not use them.

Dummy cigarettes

A plastic look-a-like that lasts between 1-3 months, Provides the hand-to-mouth stimulation of smoking. They do not help with the physical withdrawal symptoms. They are of no proven benefit, but they are not shown to be harmful.

Herbal cigarettes

Again these provide the activity of smoking without the nicotine, so they do not help with withdrawal symptoms. They still contain tar and poisonous carbon monoxide gas which are found in ordinary cigarettes and which cause considerable damage to your health. The idea is that you eliminate nicotine from your system whilst still having the behaviour of smoking the herbal cigarette, and you cut down on them over a 3-month period. There is no proven evidence that they are effective.

Filters

Put on the end of a cigarette they are designed to remove some of the tar and nicotine before you inhale. Yet smokers tend to compensate for the drop in nicotine by puffing longer and harder or even covering up the filter to stop it working so well. They are meant to help you adjust to less nicotine – but as with cutting down they have not been shown to work.

Mouthwash

Mouthwash is supposed to work by making cigarettes taste unpleasant. The product recommends you gargle with it for about 15 seconds whenever you feel a strong desire to smoke. It affects the taste of cigarettes for three to four hours, but it also adversely affects the taste of food for about half an hour. The product is not clinically proven and pregnant women are advised to check with their doctor before using it.

Alternative therapies

Some people claim to be helped by alternative therapies. However, the results of research are not clear, so overall their effectiveness remains unproven. The two most popular forms are hypnotherapy and acu-puncture. If you decide to try alternative therapy, it is important to find a registered practitioner.

The Institute of Complementary Medicine, PO Box 194, London SE16 7QZ. Tel: 020 7237 5165. Web site: www.icmedicine.co.uk or

The British Complementary Medicine Association, Kensington House, 33 Imperial Square, Cheltenham, GL50 1QZ. Tel: 0845 345 5977. Web site: www.bcma.co.uk Can both supply further information on the services available and details of local practitioners.

QUIT will not accept responsibility for referrals or advice offered by either of these bodies. Clients are strongly advised to satisfy themselves regarding the competence, registra-

tion, insurance and background of any complementary therapist.

Diet and exercise

Both of these have an important effect on your body. Stopping smoking is a major change for your body to adapt to, and a healthy diet and regular exercise suitable to your level of fitness, may help your body cope with withdrawal and boost your sense of self-confidence and well-being. There is now some evidence that regular light exercise can help people to stop smoking.

Cutting down or stopping outright?

All the evidence suggests that cutting down is much less likely to work than simply stopping outright. The last 6-10 cigarettes are very hard to give up and you will probably puff longer and harder on them so there is no real health gain. Unfortunately, even if you do manage to cut down, the numbers tend to creep back up again. So once you have planned ahead and chosen your date, it is better to stop outright.

• The above information is from QUIT's web site which can be found at www.quit.org.uk

Poor health 'the only reason that a smoker quits'

he warnings on cigarette packets that smoking kills don't work. Neither do chilling campaigns on television.

Even when the habit makes a close family member ill, the average smoker takes no notice. The only thing that will make a smoker give up is the state of his or her own health, a study said yesterday.

Researchers who examined the habits of 8,500 people over ten years found that 'people respond to their own worsening health by reducing their smoking or even quitting, but they don't respond in the same way to the declining health of other smokers, even if they live in the same household'.

The findings suggest government-backed anti-smoking campaigns costing scores of millions over the last three decades have had little impact. Even emotionally disturbing campaigns, such as the New Year TV adverts featuring model Christy Turlington talking of her father's death from lung cancer, are likely to have minimal effect, according to the study.

By Steve Doughty, Social Affairs Correspondent

Andrew Clark and Fabrice Etile, who researched the report for the Institute for Social and Economic Research, found that in a household, for instance, 'there appears to be no effect of health changes among other smokers'.

Even failing health will not persuade some smokers to cut back or quit. Smoking is linked to a lack of psychological well-being

Instead, 'the analysis indicates broadly that those whose health worsens will smoke less in future and are more likely to stop'.

They said: 'Health policy may work better if it targets smokers individually, for example, through an interview with a doctor, rather than using depersonalised campaigns.'

Even failing health will not persuade some smokers to cut back or quit. Smoking is linked to a lack of psychological well-being, say the researchers.

Since declining health can bring a psychological decline, some sickening smokers do not cut down.

Older men tend to be the most likely to quit. Young women – focus of much official concern – tend to stop as they get older, irrespective of their health, the study says.

It adds: 'Apocryphal stories abound about Uncle X who smoked 40 a day and lived to 92.

'Individuals wonder if they will be one of the lucky ones or whether smoking will affect their health much earlier and more drastically.

'The conclusion here is that what happens to you matters, whereas less notice is taken of what happens to others.'

Some facts about smoking and smokers

Information from the Roy Castle Lung Cancer Foundation

Some facts about stopping smoking

When people quit smoking they:

- Have to deal with the withdrawal from nicotine, and breaking the habit of 'lighting up'.
- May experience all sorts of different withdrawal symptoms. Not everyone gets withdrawal symptoms, but the most common ones are:

1. The craving to smoke.
2. Irritability/mood swings/feelings of emptiness.
3. Dizziness/light-headedness.
4. Headaches.
5. Inability to concentrate.
6. Sleeplessness.
7. Tiredness/feeling of exhaustion.
8. Upset stomach.
9. Mouth ulcers.
10. Sore tongue.
11. Worsened cough.
12. Tingling sensations.
13. Constipation.

Quitters won't experience all of these symptoms, but those they do experience are not imagined, nor are they simply an excuse for smoking again.

How can you help the quitter?

1. Encourage them by telling them how well they are doing, rather than how 'easy' it is to quit.

2. Remind quitters how much better they are looking – comment on any POSITIVE things such as improved breathing.

3. Keep praising and encouraging them, even though they appear to be coping well – it can still be tough after a few weeks.

4. If the quitter does not want to talk about quitting – do not force them.

5. Do not tease or tempt the quitter as this could cause a setback.

6. Do everything you can to take pressure off the quitter.

7. Remember that the quitter may be irritable so try not to snap back.

8. Do not suggest the quitter has a cigarette just to avoid a temper tantrum, instead praise their courage in quitting.

9. Some quitters worry about putting on weight, encourage them to eat a range of healthy snacks. (See Roy Castle FAG ENDS leaflet *Everybody puts on Weight – WRONG!*)

10. Try to help the quitter find activities to keep them busy and active.

- Smoking is not just a habit – it is an addiction. Smokers are actually addicted to the nicotine in their cigarettes.
- Most smokers know what smoking could do to their bodies.
- Smokers who are trying to quit will benefit from support and encouragement rather than criticism and disapproval.
- Two-thirds of smokers wish they had never started smoking and would like to stop.

Help to quit is available from

Roy Castle FAGENDS is a community voluntary group which aims to provide additional support within communities for people who are trying to cut down smoking, stop smoking or stay stopped. What do we offer?

We offer free stop-smoking support in the following ways:

- Trained staff operate a telephone helpline.
- We hold weekly self-help group meetings/drop-ins.
- We provide individual support.
- We run stop-smoking courses at various venues.

Contact us on freephone helpline 0800 195 2131

Patch them young

Nicotine therapy for smokers of 12 as children by the hundred take up the habit every day

By Beezy Marsh,
Medical Reporter

Smokers as young as 12 are to be given nicotine patches to help them kick the habit.

In a project supported by the two biggest cancer charities, a team of experts is to target young smokers to investigate whether nicotine replacement therapy (NRT) can help them quit.

If successful, the Cancer Research Campaign and Imperial Cancer Research Fund will recommend that the new programme be extended to towns and cities across the UK in an attempt to cut the number of deaths from smoking-related illnesses.

Medical licensing laws mean that NRT is not generally recommended for use by anyone under 16.

But a recent Government White Paper acknowledges that there are no clear reasons why child smokers should not use NRT products.

According to latest research, around 450 children start smoking every day. By 15, almost one in four children is a regular smoker.

Researchers plan to make patches available to young smokers in Nottingham and chart their progress.

The experts will be working with counsellors and project workers at The Zone, a youth project based on the Broxtowe estate – which is one of the city's most disadvantaged areas.

'We hope that our study will show that, as expected, NRT is just as effective in teenagers as adults in helping them to quit'

About 250 children and young people use the centre each week. Many of them have been excluded from school, the majority are smokers, and most would like to give up.

In the coming six months young people who want to quit smoking will volunteer to take part in the trial.

Professor John Britton, of the Cancer Research Campaign, who is co-ordinating the trial, said: 'At the moment we have the absurd situation that kids can easily get hold of cigarettes, but can't obtain the NRT that might help them give up.

'We hope that our study will show that, as expected, NRT is just as effective in teenagers as adults in helping them to quit.'

Professor Martin Jarvis, from the Imperial Cancer Research Fund's Health Behaviour Unit, said: 'Young people from poorer backgrounds take up smoking at an earlier age and go on to become more nicotine dependent than affluent smokers.

'Children become addicted to the nicotine in cigarettes in the same way as adults, and they experience the same withdrawal symptoms.'

Smoking is the single greatest cause of preventable illness and early death in the UK, with more than 120,000 people dying each year from smoking-related illnesses, including lung cancer and heart disease.

Nearly 80 per cent of smokers take up the habit before they are 20.

© *The Daily Mail*
October, 2001

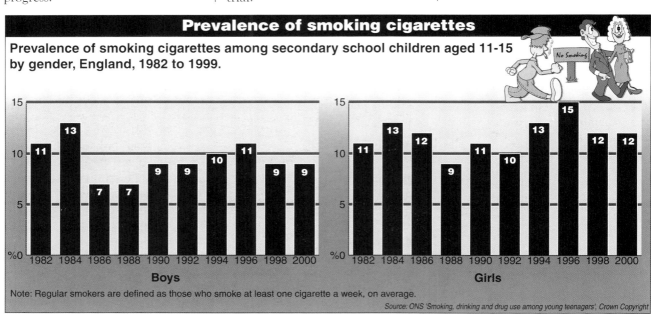

Prevalence of smoking cigarettes

Prevalence of smoking cigarettes among secondary school children aged 11-15 by gender, England, 1982 to 1999.

Boys

Girls

Note: Regular smokers are defined as those who smoke at least one cigarette a week, on average.

Source: ONS 'Smoking, drinking and drug use among young teenagers', Crown Copyright

Doubts over treatment by nicotine replacement

**By Roger Highfield,
Science Editor**

Nicotine is potentially harmful in its own right and can promote tumour growth and narrowing arteries, scientists reported yesterday.

The discovery, from experiments on human cells and mice, may have serious implications for nicotine-based therapies.

However, anti-smoking campaigners and the researchers themselves urged people not to abandon nicotine patches or chewing gum since the risks associated with smoking were so enormous.

Nicotine makes cigarettes addictive, but it is generally regarded as relatively harmless compared with substances in tobacco tar linked with lung cancer and heart disease.

But work reported in *Nature Medicine* by Dr John Cooke and colleagues at Stanford University School of Medicine, California, shows that nicotine may also be harmful.

They conducted tests on human endothelial cells, which line the walls of blood vessels and organs. Nicotine significantly increased the cells' ability to multiply while reducing the number which naturally died.

Nicotine 'patches' were placed under the skin of mice modelling a variety of human conditions – artery disease, inflammation, blood starvation in the limbs, and cancer.

In all cases, and at concentrations found in smokers, the drug stimulated the growth of new blood vessels. This was accompanied by an accelerated growth of cancer tumours and fatty deposits on artery walls.

Nicotine replacement products for quitting smokers, such as patches, gum and sprays, have been shown to be safe in clinical trials. But the scientists suggest this might be because nicotine replacement is usually brief.

The risks could be different for other nicotine uses now being considered, such as treating Alzheimer's and Parkinson's disease.

However, Dr Cooke said: 'The benefits of replacement therapy [to stop smoking] outweigh the risks.'

Clive Bates, director of the anti-tobacco group Ash, said: 'There's always a balance between risk and benefit with any sort of treatment. You expose yourself to a little danger in the hope of reducing a much larger risk to your health.'

Dr Mary Berrington, of the Cancer Research Campaign, said: 'This research does raise concerns that nicotine therapy could accelerate or worsen some diseases.'

I don't want to stop smoking!

It's OK if you don't feel ready to stop smoking just yet. But if you'd like to think more about your smoking then read on:

1. **Talk to someone about what it's like to be a smoker.**
Talk about the reasons why you want to carry on smoking and what is keeping you smoking. You could find someone to talk to at your local health centre or your local pharmacist or even a friend.

2. **Do you have a friend or colleague who has recently stopping smoking?**
Ask them how they did it, how they feel now and what situations they find helpful or tricky.

3. **Ask someone close to you what they think about your smoking.**
Try to hear what they say as concern for you and not as criticism. If you want to find out more about smoking and health then you could contact your doctor or nurse or one of the smokers' helplines.

4. **Ask yourself whether you still want to be a smoker in five or ten years' time.**
How much will you have spent on smoking by then? What could your life be like as a non-smoker? What would be the benefits of stopping smoking?

5. **If you want evidence that smoking is doing you harm, get your carbon monoxide level tested.**
Smokers have lots more of this poison in their bodies than non-smokers.

Most people who quit don't just stop smoking automatically. They go through different stages from not wanting to quit, to thinking about quitting, to planning to quit, to quitting and then to staying a non-smoker. Many people go through these stages a few times, finding out what helps them stop smoking and what doesn't. By just reading the above information you've already taken small steps. You've started thinking about your smoking – maybe you're more ready than you thought?

• The above information is an extract from the No Smoking Day web site which can be found at www.nosmokingday.org.uk

Top ten tips

Information from No Smoking Day

1. Set a date and time to stop and stick to it

Try to avoid a day that will be stressful. No Smoking Day is an ideal time to quit as you will be in the company of thousands of other smokers all aiming to give up

2. Prepare to stop smoking

Get rid of lighters, ashtrays and matches and make sure you don't have any cigarettes around. Remove any stale smoke smells by spring cleaning your house and clothes.

3. Write down all the reasons you want to quit

This can include saving money, being healthier, for the sake of your family. Carry this list around with you as a reminder when you are tempted to have a cigarette.

4. Don't be afraid to ask for help

Let friends and family know you're giving up smoking and ask them to be understanding. Your GP, nurse or pharmacist will give you advice on how to quit, and you can always call one of the smokers' helplines.

5. Do it with others

Find others who would like to give

www.**nosmokingday**.org.uk

Make it a day to remember

up and agree to support each other. Keep in daily contact and make a pact not to let each other down.

6. Ease the withdrawal symptoms

Nicotine is addictive, and you may experience withdrawal symptoms, for example irritability, lack of concentration and sleeping problems. Try to see these symptoms as your body cleaning itself and healing – remember they are only temporary. Consider using NRT.

7. Take it one day at a time

Concentrate on getting through each

> *Be prepared when someone offers you a cigarette and take pride in saying 'No thank you – I don't smoke'*

day without a cigarette. Be prepared when someone offers you a cigarette and take pride in saying 'No thank you – I don't smoke'.

8. Break the links that create the habit

Smokers agree that there are certain situations strongly linked to their habit, for example smoking after a meal or when having a drink. Try to avoid these situations if you think you will be tempted to smoke or do something different, for example go for a short walk after a meal.

9. Reward yourself

Save the money that you would have spent on cigarettes on a treat such as a new outfit, going out for a meal or taking a holiday.

10. Once stopped, stay stopped

Remember that 'just one cigarette' will lead to another. Keep reminding yourself of the health and other benefits of giving up smoking.

• The above information is an extract from the No Smoking Day web site which can be found at www.nosmokingday.org.uk

© No Smoking Day

Kicking the habit

Information from the Coronary Prevention Group

Smoking is the largest single cause of premature death in the world, and every single smoking-related death is entirely preventable. Every cigarette smoked takes around 7 minutes off your life and results in smokers losing an average of $7\frac{1}{2}$ years of their lives.

In Britain over two-thirds of smokers want to quit and every year over 3 million try. To date there are over 11 million success stories; for every three men you see in the street, one is a successful ex-smoker. Quitting takes determination but it is within your reach.

Stop day
Convince yourself that you really want to give up, that you will succeed, and then choose a day to stop, and stop completely on this day. (Choose a time when you are not under too much stress.)

Throw away your cigarettes
And all the paraphernalia that goes with them such as lighters and ash trays.

Tell everyone
Make a point of telling people you have given up so that they can support you. It may also be helpful to give up with a friend.

Take it a day at a time
Each day just try for one more day. Identify the times when you normally have a cigarette and make sure you have something else to do (like the washing up!).

Ash cash
Work out how much money you are saving and treat yourself!

Quash the cravings
Store your last few butts in a screw-top jar and whenever you get a craving open it up and take a good, deep, off-putting breath.

Think positive
You are a non-smoker, not an ex-smoker. When offered a cigarette say 'No thanks, I don't smoke'.

Giving up smoking can be unpleasant as your body does its best to convince you that you need nicotine. Remember that you don't, and won't be a slave to the addiction. The feelings of irritability, insomnia and depression will pass and be

> *Giving up smoking can be unpleasant as your body does its best to convince you that you need nicotine. Remember that you don't*

replaced by a great feeling of achievement and new lease of life. Likewise, any increase in weight is likely to be small and temporary as long as you eat sensibly and give your new and improved lungs a regular workout by exercising.

The benefits of quitting smoking are enormous and far outweigh the short-term discomforts. Everything from your wallet to your skin will benefit and within 10 years your risk of a heart attack is the same as a lifelong non-smoker's.

Remember, quitting smoking is the single best thing you can do to improve your health. Good luck!
• If you have questions or comments e-mail us at cpg@lshtm.ac.uk

© Healthnet – 1995/2000

EU gets tough to stub out smoking

By Ambrose Evans-Pritchard in Strasbourg

Euro-MPs approved draconian anti-smoking laws yesterday which will lower tar levels and lead to stark health warnings on cigarette packets at least five times the current size.

From September next year, a third of the packet will be taken up with bold black-and-white warnings such as 'Smoking kills' or 'Smoking seriously harms others around you, especially children'.

On the back, 40 per cent will be taken up with detailed descriptions of smoking-related diseases. Terms such as 'mild', 'light' or 'low tar' will be prohibited, to avoid giving smokers a false impression of safety.

Maximum tar levels will be reduced from 12 to 10 milligrammes per cigarette. Nicotine levels will be reduced to one milligramme. Britain and other EU states will be encouraged to compel manufactures to add shocking pictures of putrid gums and blackened lungs.

The MEP Catherine Stihler, Labour's health spokesman, said the new rules were the toughest in the world. 'The days of glamorous cigarette packs with obscure warnings are over. Smoking will never be the same again,' she said. The new laws will also ban the manufacture of high-tar cigarettes for the export market.

The UK Tobacco Manufacturers' Association said the law would force UK firms in Darlington and Southampton to move their factories abroad, costing up to 4,000 British jobs. Euro-MPs are furious that they cannot stop Brussels spending £650 million of taxpayers' money a year subsidising tobacco production in Greece, Spain and Italy.

© Telegraph Group Limited, London 2001

I'm your cigarette packet, can we have a little chat?

For smokers still in doubt about the health risks involved in each puff, a loud reminder is on the way. Molins, one of Britain's leading suppliers to the tobacco industry, has secretly developed a cigarette packet that talks.

The firm has applied for a patent for the idea, which was developed by engineers at its Coventry research centre. A tiny speaker concealed within the packet is activated each time the lid is opened.

New Scientist magazine, which discovered the unpublicised patent application, reports this week that the speaker could deliver a cancer warning 'in any of several languages'. Alternatively, it could play a tune, such as the funeral march or the Police hit 'Every Breath You Take'.

Molins' finance director, David Cowen, said: 'It's quite a neat idea which may or may not have a commercial use.'

The company supplies machines used in the production of cigarettes. Its customers include the world's top tobacco companies, including British American Tobacco, Gallaher and Imperial Tobacco.

Mr Cowen admitted that the idea of a singing cigarette packet might get a cool reception from the major manufacturers. 'I think it's unlikely that the funeral march is what customers would want.'

The concept is a long way from reaching newsagents' shelves. He said: 'We don't have a patent yet – that's a process which can take up to four years. This is one of many applications filed by Molins. It's just an idea, developed in the normal course of business.'

There was a muted response yesterday from the tobacco industry, which is already smouldering this week from a decision by the European Union to increase the size of written health warnings on packets.

A spokesman for BAT said: 'We've not seen this box yet so it's

difficult to comment. But if we were approached, I'm sure we'd look at it.'

Gallaher, best known for Benson & Hedges and Silk Cut, said: 'We're not going to comment on another company's patent ideas.'

One of Britain's leading suppliers to the tobacco industry has secretly developed a cigarette packet that talks

---

Anti-smoking activists were more positive. Amanda Sandford of Action on Smoking and Health said: 'A tinny voice telling you to quit smoking is a bit gimmicky. I'm not sure people would take it seriously. But if it does ever come to fruition, it wouldn't be such a bad idea.'

She added: 'I can't see it happening if it's left to the industry to do voluntarily. They would have to make audible health warnings compulsory.'

The technology used in the gadget is similar to devices used in talking greetings cards. A stiff plastic strip is stuck on the hinged lid of the cigarette packet. When extended, this activates a microchip, which powers a tiny microphone hidden in the base.

Smokers have some experience of noisy devices: musical lighters have been available for many years.

Molins, which has its headquarters in Milton Keynes, hit hard times in the 1990s when the south-east Asian economic crisis triggered sharp cutbacks in the tobacco industry.

Although its main business is supplying the tobacco industry, the firm also makes machines for other purposes. It hit the headlines in 1996 by coming up with the technology to make the world's first pyramid-shaped tea bag, the PG Tips tetrahedron.

• By Andrew Clark

Do you want to help someone give up smoking?

How you can help

www.nosmokingday.org.uk
Make it a day to remember

No matter what you do, you can't force someone to stop if they don't want to. But if your friend/partner/relative wants to give it a go, you can try to make things a bit easier for them. Here are some ideas for how you can help your friend/partner/relative Kiss it Goodbye on No Smoking Day:

- Discuss their habit and their commitment to stopping.
- Don't threaten, nag or lecture about the dangers of smoking – focus on the benefits they'll get if they give up, e.g. more money, better health.
- Show your companion that you care and have an interest in keeping them healthy.
- Take a trip down to your local pharmacist with them to find out if any of the NRT treatments available could work for them (and check out the 'smokers' section for more info on the products available to help).
- Encourage them to call a national helpline for more information about stopping (if they are a bit shy, maybe you could offer to do it for them).
- Send a card on the Day to wish them good luck.
- Make up a Kiss it Goodbye survival kit to help them through the Day. It could include a leaflet or booklet about how to stop smoking, sugar-free gum, low-calorie snacks like carrots and fruit, distractions such as games or puzzles, a toothbrush and toothpaste and a treat (such as a ticket to the cinema for the end of the day).
- Take them out to breakfast or lunch.
- If temptation strikes, remind them why they decided to stop. Stress the benefits of stopping rather than the dangers of smoking.

- Be sympathetic during the hard times – it's common to be edgy when stopping smoking.
- Make sure that you are available in person or by telephone. Keep in touch – but avoid pestering as they may be managing fine!
- Slip-ups are normal but having one or two cigarettes doesn't mean failure. Help your companion to get back their motivation and to look out for danger situations in the future.

- Plan an evening activity that avoids the temptation to smoke – perhaps swimming or the cinema. It's probably best to avoid the pub if they normally associate smoking with alcohol.
- Give praise and encouragement and at the end of the Day, congratulations.
- If your friend has decided to stop for good, plan a shopping trip after a week or two. They can buy something special with the money saved by not smoking.

- The above information is an extract from the No Smoking Day web site which can be found at www.nosmokingday.org.uk

© No Smoking Day

Smoking amongst adults

The prevalence of cigarette smoking has dropped substantially since 1978 (from 40%), although it levelled off in the 1990s.

16- 24-year-olds

25- 34-year-olds

35- 49-year-olds

50 and over

Source: ONS 'General Household Survey 1978-1998', Crown Copyright

Jab that could end the craving for a cigarette

Smokers could become immune to the effects of nicotine thanks to a vaccine developed by British scientists.

The vaccine, the world's first against cigarette addiction, is about to be tested in clinical trials.

If successful, smokers could soon give up cigarettes for good with the help of a simple injection.

Surveys show three out of four of Britain's 13 million smokers want to quit.

Xenova, the Cambridge-based biotechnology company behind the jab, envisages it will be used to help smokers give up rather than inoculate non-smokers against developing the urge.

John St Clair Roberts, the company's medical director, said the vaccine works by 'mopping up' nicotine before it reaches the brain and triggers the body's addiction responses.

The result is that nicotine never reaches the brain and does not produce any effect. The smoker might as well be smoking air.

'The is the first time an anti-smoking vaccine has gone under clinical trials,' said Mr St Clair Roberts.

'We are trying to keep nicotine out of the brain, unlike other nicotine replacement therapies, so you are not reinforcing the addiction.'

He said the vaccine works because nicotine molecules are so small they are not recognised by the immune system.

TA-NIC alters the immune system so it recognises the nicotine molecules and produces antibodies.

Mr St Clair Roberts said the phase one study will assess the safety and tolerability of the vaccine in 60 patients, both smokers and non-smokers.

'It is not intended as an efficacy study but a safety study,' he said.

It will be carried out in Belgium and the company hopes to have obtained 'preliminary data' by Easter.

Over one billion worldwide smoke tobacco products, resulting in approximately three million deaths a year from smoking-related diseases.

David Oxlade, Xenova's chief executive, said: 'Most people who want to stop smoking find it very hard to do so, even though they may be aware of the risks involved.

'Although at an early stage of development, if TA-NIC can be of assistance it could have an important contribution to make in reducing the burdens that smoking imposes.'

Clive Bates, director of the anti-smoking group ASH, said: 'A nicotine vaccine would be a profound development, which would effectively become one of the most important medicines in the response to cancer, lung and heart disease.'

Xenova has been working on the vaccine for more than three years.

Experiments on animals in the laboratory have indicated that using the immune system approach does work. The move to human trials is an indication of the company's confidence.

• By James Chapman, Science Correspondent

'We are trying to keep nicotine out of the brain, unlike other nicotine replacement therapies, so you are not reinforcing the addiction'

Up in smoke, the myth that tobacco helps fight stress

The idea that smoking relieves stress is a myth, say psychologists.

Rather than help smokers relax, nicotine actually increases anxiety and tension, they claim.

The relaxing effect of smoking is a psychological addiction, warn researchers at the University of East London.

When combined with a chemical addiction to nicotine, levels of stress are heightened, not lowered. Psychologist Andy Parrott, whose findings have been published in the medical journal *American Psychologist*, explained: 'Regular smokers need nicotine to maintain normal moods as they suffer tension between cigarettes.'

Dr Parrott examined more than 30 international studies into smoking and stress.

He said: 'Most smokers mistakenly claim cigarettes are helping to relieve stress.'

The psychologist said regular smoking halts the onset of withdrawal symptoms, creating a psychological link between cigarettes and feeling good.

He called on the Government's anti-smoking campaigns to shatter the myth that cigarettes relieve stress.

Dr Parrott said: 'This could help many people kick the habit.'

His comments were backed by anti-smoking pressure group ASH.

Clive Bates, director of ASH, said: 'All that smokers experience is a relief from their addiction. This dependency gradually disappears when they quit.'

Nearly 13 million Britons smoke, despite more than 100,000 deaths each year from lung cancer, heart disease and respiratory illnesses caused by cigarettes.

Smoking and your heart

Information from the Coronary Prevention Group

Smoking causes serious damage to your health. It causes heart disease and many cancers, including lung cancer. 111,000 people in the UK die every year from smoking-related diseases, 46,000 of these from cancers due to smoking. Smoking causes 30,000 deaths from coronary heart disease and many more people suffer years of pain and discomfort from angina.

How does smoking affect your heart?

Cigarette smoke contains several thousand chemicals, at least two of which – carbon monoxide and nicotine – are thought to be involved in causing coronary heart disease.

Carbon monoxide is a poisonous gas (also present in car exhaust fumes) and is picked up by the blood much more readily than oxygen. So, when carbon monoxide is present, there is less 'room' for oxygen in the blood. The oxygen-carrying capacity of a smoker's blood can be cut by up to 15%. This means that the heart has to work much harder to get enough oxygen all around the body.

Nicotine stimulates the nervous system and this leads to an increase in the rate the heart beats at and causes the blood vessels to narrow. This again puts a strain on the heart. Nicotine also makes the blood 'sticky' and more likely to clot and block the blood vessels.

A cigarette smoker has about double the risk of having a heart attack as a non-smoker. For the smoker who has high blood pressure and high cholesterol, the risk is eight times greater.

Women who smoke are at especially high risk of heart disease if they also take the contraceptive pill.

Is it too late to give up?

No – whatever your age, it is never too late to give up. Giving up drastically reduces the risk of a heart attack; within 5 years your risk is half that of a smoker and after 10 years it is the same as a non-smoker's. Giving up is especially important for those who have already had a heart attack.

Smoking causes 30,000 deaths from coronary heart disease and many more people suffer years of pain and discomfort from angina

---

But there are other advantages too: you reduce your risk of lung cancer and lung diseases such as emphysema. You will be able to breathe more easily, have a better sense of taste and smell and feel fitter. Your complexion will improve and you'll have a lot more money in your pocket!

How do you stop smoking?

There is no magic answer to quitting but the following tips may be helpful
- Convince yourself that you really want to give up smoking and that you will succeed.
- Choose a time when you are not under too much stress.
- Give up with a friend.
- Throw away all your cigarettes.
- Make a point of telling people that you have given up.

- Work out how much money you are saving and put that amount aside each week.
- Make a big effort not to smoke after meals.
- For more advice and support ring the Government helpline on 0800 169 0 169

People who change to low tar cigarettes tend to inhale more to maintain their nicotine intake. As they inhale more they may increase the amount of carbon monoxide absorbed. So, although they may reduce their risk of lung cancer, their risk of heart disease may increase.

What are the side effects of giving up?

Quitting is difficult because the body is addicted to nicotine. Consequently, when you give up you may become irritable, depressed or restless and have difficulty concentrating. These feelings will pass though and it is important to persevere as the benefits will last a lifetime.

Many people worry about gaining weight when they quit smoking. This is not inevitable but many quitters do gain a little weight, six to eight pounds on average. The first thing to remember is don't go on a crash diet but be careful not to replace your cigarettes with lots of sweet or fatty snacks. If you need to nibble on something choose fruit. Secondly, the risk to your health of a few extra pounds is small compared to the risks of smoking – it is not worth smoking to keep your weight down. Those pounds can easily be lost by eating healthily and exercising.

Above all, be positive and you will join the ranks of the 11,000,000 people in the UK who have successfully given up.

- If you have questions or comments e-mail us at cpg@lshtm.ac.uk

© Healthnet – 1995/2000

The fatal attraction

Information from SCAPE

Introduction

Cigarettes falsely appear to offer women an answer to their problems and insecurities. You may view your cigarettes as your last token of rebellion or an invaluable companion who waits with you when your date is late, or even an escape from your stressful life.

However, cigarettes do not keep their promises. Once this disillusionment sets in you realise that you are addicted to a fatal relationship. More than 70% of female smokers would like to stop, so why do so many continue to smoke?

Like ending any relationship, an important step in your path to successfully finish with nicotine is to understand your relationship. Only then will you be able to see that cigarettes are not the answer to your problems. Cigarette smoking kills one in two smokers and therefore life without cigarettes will be both better and longer!

Emotion

Women are more emotionally dependent on cigarettes than men and are more likely to think of cigarettes as their main source of pleasure. Almost half of women who smoke feel they are unable to cope without cigarettes.

Stress

Over a quarter of women smoke to help them cope with stress.

Weight

Women's greatest fear about stopping smoking is putting on weight.

Image

Women are image conscious smokers. Studies of advertising influence show that more women than men choose cigarette brands for image reasons.

Action

Women are more likely than men to report the sensation of holding a cigarette and bringing the cigarette to their lips, as a reason for smoking.

Control

Women have been found to smoke to control their mood, for example, smoking to control unpleasant feelings such as anxiety, or for pleasure.

• The above information is an extract from the publication *Fatal Attraction – Lifting the Smokescreen*, produced by the Smoking Cessation in Primary carE (SCAPE) Taskforce. See page 41 for their address details.

© Smoking Cessation in Primary carE (SCAPE) Taskforce

Lifting the smokescreen

Information from SCAPE

Smoking and beauty

Although you probably spend a small fortune on keeping (or making!) yourselves beautiful, you continue to damage your skin by smoking.

One of the best understood side effects of smoking is that it can lead to premature wrinkling – you have probably all seen smokers in their 40s who look like they are 20 years older.

However, smoking has a much greater negative impact on your skin than you may have thought. It has been shown that appearance is negatively affected by cigarette smoke in the following ways.

Greyish waste appearance

Smoking restricts blood vessels, reducing the amount of blood flowing to the skin and depriving it of oxygen and essential nutrients.

Loss of elasticity

Smoking increases the production of an enzyme that breaks down collagen in the skin. Loss of collagen speeds up the ageing process, causing a loss of suppleness and premature wrinkling.

Gauntness

Smokers may develop hollow cheeks through repeated sucking on cigarettes, this is particularly noticeable in underweight smokers.

Bad breath

Smoking is a cause of bad breath.

Premature wrinkling

Squinting to prevent smoke getting in your eyes and puckering to draw on a cigarette causes further wrinkling around the eyes and mouth.

Discoloration

Prolonged smoking causes yellowing of the teeth and discolouration of the fingers and fingernails on the hand used to hold cigarettes.

• The above information is an extract from the publication *Fatal Attraction – Lifting the Smokescreen*, produced by the Smoking Cessation in Primary carE (SCAPE) Taskforce. See page 41 for their address details.

© Smoking Cessation in Primary carE (SCAPE) Taskforce

ADDITIONAL RESOURCES

You might like to contact the following organisations for further information. Due to the increasing cost of postage, many organisations cannot respond to enquiries unless they receive a stamped, addressed envelope.

ASH – Action on Smoking and Health
102 Clifton Street
London, EC2A 4HW
Tel: 020 7739 5902
Fax: 020 7613 0531
Web site: www.ash.org.uk
ASH was set up to press for changes in society that would reduce the harm caused by smoking.

The Cancer Research Campaign (CRC)
10 Cambridge Terrace
London, NW1 4JL
Tel: 020 7224 1333
Fax: 020 7487 4310
Web site: www.crc.org.uk
Works to attack and defeat the disease of cancer in all its forms.

The Coronary Prevention Group
2 Taviton Street
London, WC1H 0BT
Tel: 020 7927 2125
Fax: 020 7927 2127
Web site: www.healthnet.org.uk
Contributes to the prevention of coronary heart disease, the UK's major cause of death.

FORCES International
Web site: www.worldsmokersday.org
World Smokers Day is an initiative launched by FORCES International whose web site can be found at www.forces.org

FOREST (Freedom Organisation for the Right to Enjoy Smoking)
Audley House, 13 Palace Street
London, SW1E 5HX
Tel: 020 7233 6144
Fax: 020 7630 6226
Web site: www.forest-on-smoking.org.uk
Defends adult freedom of choice against prohibitionists, social authoritarians and medical paternalists. FOREST does not promote smoking. FOREST will provide further information upon receipt of a formal request from teachers but will not supply information to any person under the age of 18 years.

National Asthma Campaign
Providence House
Providence Place
London, N1 0NT
Tel: 020 7226 2260
Fax: 020 7704 0740
E-mail: info@asthma.org.uk
Web site: www.asthma.org.uk
The National Asthma Campaign is the independent charity working to conquer asthma. Runs the Asthma Helpline on 0845 7 01 02 03 for confidential advice on asthma from their team of asthma nurse specialists.

No Smoking Day
Unit 203, 16 Baldwin Gardens
London, EC1N 7RJ
Tel: 020 7916 8070
Fax: 020 7916 7556
E-mail: mail@nosmokingday.org.uk
Web site: www.nosmokingday.org.uk
A national campaign organised by a committee of 14 agencies representing a collaboration of public, professional and voluntary partners, all with an interest in reducing smoking-related disease. Produces an annual campaign pack which includes leaflets and factsheets.

QUIT
Victory House
170 Tottenham Court Road
London, W1P 0HA
Tel: 020 7388 5775
Fax: 020 7388 5995
E-mail: quit-projects@clara.co.uk
Web site: www.quit.org.uk
Helps smokers to try to give up. Runs Stop Smoking groups for the general public and in-house for the workplace. For help and advice on how to stop smoking, ring their freephone Quitline on 0800 00 22 00.

The Roy Castle Lung Cancer Foundation
International Centre for Lung Cancer Research
200 London Road
Liverpool, L3 9TA
Tel: 0151 794 8800
Fax: 0151 794 8888
E-mail: roycastle@enterprise.net
Web site: www.roycastle.org
A UK charity and research centre, dedicated to defeating lung cancer. Also runs the Kids Against Tobacco Smoke (KATS) education service.

Smoking Cessation in Primary carE (SCAPE) Taskforce
Cohn and Wolfe
30 Orange Street
London, WC2 7LZ
Tel: 020 7331 5300
Web site:
www.liftingthesmokescreen.org.uk
A group of primary care healthcare professionals with a special interest in smoking cessation. Runs the campaign 'Fatal Attraction, Lifting the Smokescreen'.

Tobacco Manufacturers' Association (TMA)
55 Tufton Street, Westminster
London, SW1P 3QL
Tel: 020 7544 0100
Fax: 020 7544 0117
E-mail: information@the-tma.org.uk
Web site: www.the-tma.org.uk
The TMA is the trade association for those companies which manufacture tobacco products in the UK.

UNISON
1 Mabledon Place
London, WC1H 9AJ
Tel: 020 7388 2366
Web site: www.unison.org.uk
Represents and organises people who work in public services, for private companies which provide services to the public or for voluntary organisations.

INDEX

acupuncture, quitting smoking through 26
advertising, tobacco products 3, 7
age
    and smoking
        in children 4, 32
        prevalence of 37
        proof-of-age cards 7
        young people 1, 37
air pollution, and tobacco smoke 12
allergy to tobacco 15
alternative therapies, for quitting smoking 26, 29-30
Alzheimer's disease, and nicotine 33
asthma
    and smoking 2
        passive smoking 12, 15

babies, and passive smoking 3, 5, 13
boys, and smoking 1, 32
breast cancer, and smoking 1

cancer
    risk reduction after stopping smoking 25
    and smoking 1
    see also lung cancer
childminders, and smoking 17
children
    and smoking 1, 2, 4, 7
        living with parents who smoke 5
        passive smoking 3, 5, 6, 11, 12-13
        quitting 32
        risk factors 5
        statistics 5, 32

death
    from smoking
        lung cancer 1
        passive smoking 2, 5
        rates 2, 6, 25, 38
        and women 1, 2
        and young people 6
deprivation, and smoking 4-5
diet, and quitting smoking 30, 39
discrimination, against smokers 9, 10
disease
    and smoking 1, 2, 4, 5, 6, 17, 32, 39
        passive smoking 2, 5, 11, 12-13, 14, 17, 24

European Union (EU), anti-smoking laws 35, 36
exercise, and quitting smoking 30, 35, 39

families
    of smokers
        helping someone to give up 31, 37
        risk factors for smoking in children 5
film stars, and teenage smoking 8
FOREST 10, 18

    on passive smoking 14-15
    on smoking in public places 19-20
    on smoking in the workplace 23
friends, helping someone to give up smoking 31, 37

gender
    and smoking 1, 4, 11
    see also men; women
girls, and smoking 1, 32
Government policies on smoking
    anti-smoking campaigns 30
    cigarette advertising 7
    in public places 13
    reducing tar levels 24
    tobacco taxes 10
    in the workplace 3, 13, 24

health benefits, of quitting smoking 25, 39
health professionals, helping smokers to quit 3
health promotion, and no-smoking policies in the
    workplace 22
health risks
    of smoking 1, 2, 4, 5, 6, 32
        and nicotine 33
        passive smoking 2, 5, 11, 12, 16, 17, 24
        in the workplace 21
heart disease
    and smoking 1, 4, 17, 32, 39
        benefits of quitting 25, 35, 39
        passive smoking 12, 16, 17
human rights, and the Smokers' Declaration of Rights 9-10
hypnosis, quitting smoking through 26

Internet
    smoking web sites 7, 10, 11

lung cancer
    and smoking 1, 2, 32, 33, 39
        age of starting smoking 5
        low tar cigarettes 39
        passive smoking 2, 12, 14

men
    and smoking 11
        decline in 1
        quitting 30, 35

nicotine replacement therapy (NRT) 26, 27-9, 37
    and children 32
    doubts over 33
No Smoking Day 3-4, 6, 33, 34
    web site 34, 37

occupational groups, and smoking 4

parents, and smoking in schools 8
Parkinson's disease, and nicotine 33
passive smoking
    and children 3, 5, 6, 11, 12-13
        FOREST on 14-15

ACKNOWLEDGEMENTS

The publisher is grateful for permission to reproduce the following material.

While every care has been taken to trace and acknowledge copyright, the publisher tenders its apology for any accidental infringement or where copyright has proved untraceable. The publisher would be pleased to come to a suitable arrangement in any such case with the rightful owner.

Chapter One: The Issues

Smoking trends in the UK, © The Cancer Research Campaign, *Smoking: the facts*, © National Asthma Campaign, *Regular smokers*, © Crown copyright is reproduced with the permission of the Controller of Her Majesty's Stationery Office, *Smoking statistics*, © KATS (Kids Against Tobacco Smoke), The Roy Castle Lung Cancer Foundation, *What's in a cigarette*, © No Smoking Day, *Risk factors and determinants of cigarette smoking*, © Royal College of Physicians, *Young people and smoking*, © ASH – Action on Smoking and Health, *Hard facts*, © Crown copyright is reproduced with the permission of the Controller of Her Majesty's Stationery Office, *The real cost of smoking*, © No Smoking Day, *Children and smoking*, © Tobacco Manufacturers' Association (TMA), *Film icons blamed for teenage smoking*, © Guardian Newspapers Limited 2001, *School lets its pupils smoke*, © Telegraph Group Limited, London 2001, *Smokers' rights declaration*, © FORCES International, *The basic smoking debate facts and figures*, © FOREST, *Smoking affects everyone . . .* , © Crown copyright is reproduced with the permission of the Controller of Her Majesty's Stationery Office, *Cigarette smoking smong adults aged 16 and over*, © Crown copyright is reproduced with the permission of the Controller of Her Majesty's Stationery Office, *Passive smoking*, © ASH – Action on Smoking and Health, *The truth about 'passive smoking'*, © FOREST, *Half an hour of passive smoking can harm heart*, © Telegraph Group Limited, London 2001, *20 cigarettes across the EU*, © Tobacco Manufacturers' Association (TMA), *There'll soon be no smoke without ire*, © Guardian Newspapers Limited 2001, *Smoking in public places*,

© FOREST, *Smoking in the workplace*, © UNISON, *Smoking in the workplace*, © FOREST, *Pub lobby blocks ban on smoking at work*, © Guardian Newspapers Limited 2001.

Chapter Two: Ways to Quit Smoking

Stopping smoking, © ASH – Action on Smoking and Health, *The QUIT guide to stopping smoking*, © QUIT, *Poor health 'the only reason that a smoker quits'*, © The Daily Mail, July 2001, *Some facts about smoking and smokers*, © The Roy Castle Lung Cancer Foundation, *Patch them young*, © The Daily Mail, October 2001, *Prevalence of smoking cigarettes*, © Crown copyright is reproduced with the permission of the Controller of Her Majesty's Stationery Office, *Doubts over treatment by nicotine replacement*, © Telegraph Group Limited, London 2001, *I don't want to stop smoking!*, © No Smoking Day, *Top ten tips*, © No Smoking Day, *Kicking the habit*, © The Coronary Prevention Group, *EU gets tough to stub out smoking*, © Telegraph Group Limited, London 2001, *I'm your cigarette packet, can we have a little chat?*, © Guardian Newspapers Limited 2001, *Do you want to help someone give up smoking?*, © No Smoking Day, *Smoking amongst adults*, © Crown copyright is reproduced with the permission of the Controller of Her Majesty's Stationery Office, *Jab that could end the craving for a cigarette*, © The Daily Mail, September 2001, *Smoking and your heart*, © The Coronary Prevention Group, *The fatal attraction*, © Smoking Cessation in Primary carE (SCAPE) Taskforce, *Lifting the smokescreen*, © Smoking Cessation in Primary carE (SCAPE) Taskforce.

Photographs and illustrations:

Pages 1, 12, 19, 21, 24, 31: Pumpkin House, pages 4, 9, 14, 18, 23, 29, 34, 36: Simon Kneebone.

Craig Donnellan
Cambridge
January, 2002